BrightRED Study Guide

CfE ADVANCED Higher

CHEMISTRY

Archie Gibb, Dr David Hawley and Dr Shona Scheuerl

First published in 2015 by:
Bright Red Publishing Ltd
1 Torphichen Street
Edinburgh
EH3 8HX

Reprinted with corrections 2016, 2018
Copyright © Bright Red Publishing Ltd 2015

Cover image © Caleb Rutherford

A CIP record for this book is available from the British Library.

ISBN 978-1-906736-71-2

With thanks to:
PDQ Digital Media Solutions Ltd, Bungay (layout), Anne Horscroft (editorial).

Cover design and series book design by Caleb Rutherford – e i d e t i c.

Acknowledgements
Every effort has been made to seek all copyright-holders. If any have been overlooked, then
Bright Red Publishing will be delighted to make the necessary arrangements.

Permission has been sought from all relevant copyright holders and Bright Red Publishing are grateful for
the use of the following:

deyangeorgiev/iStock.com (p 28); Marcos André (CC BY 2.0)1 (p 50); anneheathen (CC BY 2.0) 1 (p 50);
Matt Biddulph (CC BY-SA 2.0) 2 (p 50); Semnic/Shutterstock.com (p 77); Exam question taken from
Advanced Higher Chemistry 2010 paper (Section A Question 3) (p 17) and Specimen Question Paper
(Section B Question 2) (p 81) © Scottish Qualifications Authority (n.b. solutions do not emanate from
the SQA).
(CC BY 2.0)1 http://creativecommons.org/licenses/by/2.0/
(CC BY-SA 2.0) 2 http://creativecommons.org/licenses/by-sa/2.0/

Printed and bound in the UK by W & G Baird.

CONTENTS

INTRODUCTION

INTRODUCING ADVANCED HIGHER CHEMISTRY

COURSE STRUCTURE

The Advanced Higher Chemistry course is divided into three units:

- Inorganic and Physical Chemistry
- Organic Chemistry and Instrumental Analysis
- Researching Chemistry

In the **Inorganic and Physical Chemistry** unit, you will discover how electromagnetic radiation is used in atomic spectroscopy to identify elements and your understanding of the concept of atomic structure will be extended by considering atomic orbitals and electronic configurations. You will learn, through electron pair theory, how to predict the shapes of molecules and ions. The physical and chemical properties of transition metals and their compounds are investigated. Your knowledge of chemical equilibria will be extended by considering the quantitative aspects of equilibria. You will also develop an understanding of the factors that influence the feasibility of chemical reactions. Your understanding of reaction rates and reaction mechanisms will be progressed by a study of reaction kinetics.

The **Organic Chemistry and Instrumental Analysis** unit will allow you to expand your knowledge and understanding of organic chemistry. You will study the structure and bonding in organic compounds and draw on this to explain their physical and chemical properties and to explain the origin of colour in some organic compounds. Key organic reaction types and mechanisms will be considered, which will allow you to devise ways of synthesising organic compounds from simpler molecules. You will also learn how elemental analysis and various spectroscopic techniques are used to verify chemical structures. This unit concludes with a study of medicines and their interactions.

The **Researching Chemistry** unit gives you the opportunity to gain an understanding of stoichiometric calculations, to develop practical skills and to carry out research in chemistry. You will develop the key skills associated with a variety of practical techniques and by using this knowledge, along with an understanding of the basic concepts, you will be able to identify, research, plan and safely carry out a practical investigation of your choice. This unit will also equip you with the scientific background and skills necessary to analyse scientific papers and to use them to make informed choices and decisions.

BENEFITS OF ADVANCED HIGHER CHEMISTRY

Advanced Higher Chemistry is a challenging, but rewarding, course. It has been devised to allow you to develop the ability to think analytically, creatively and independently, and to make reasoned evaluations. The course emphasises practical and experiential learning opportunities with a strong skills-based approach.

As well as providing an excellent grounding for the future study of chemistry and chemistry-related subjects, Advanced Higher Chemistry is highly regarded by employers.

EXTERNAL ASSESSMENT

At the end of the course you will be assessed externally by two components.

Component 1: Question paper – 100 marks (77% of the total marks)

contd

The duration of the question paper is 2 hours 30 minutes and it is divided into two sections:

- Section 1 is made up of 30 multiple-choice questions and is worth 30 marks
- Section 2 is made up of both restricted and extended response questions and is worth 70 marks

Marks will be distributed approximately proportionally across the three units and the majority of the marks will be awarded for applying knowledge and understanding. The other marks will be awarded for applying scientific enquiry and problem-solving skills. Section 2 will include two open-ended questions with three marks allocated to each. You will be able to recognise such questions by the phrase '**using your knowledge of chemistry**'. These questions will not directly assess the knowledge taught during the course, but, instead, you are to use the knowledge you do have to suggest possible answers.

Component 2: Project Report – 30 marks (23% of the total marks)

As part of the course you will investigate/research an in-depth study of a chemistry topic, chosen by you in consultation with your teacher/lecturer. In general, the project will have the following format: planning; researching; investigating; collecting and analysing data; evaluating findings; and, finally, producing a written scientific report, which will be submitted to the Scottish Qualification Authority (SQA) for marking.

INTERNAL ASSESSMENT

All three units (Inorganic and Physical Chemistry, Organic Chemistry and Instrumental Analysis and Researching Chemistry) are assessed by your teacher or lecturer. For the first two of these units, your knowledge will usually be assessed by a written test. Your school or college will also collect evidence to show that, during the course, you have demonstrated the skills of scientific enquiry necessary to carry out an experiment and have shown that you have appropriate problem-solving skills.

To pass the Researching Chemistry unit, as well as demonstrating a knowledge of the skills included, you will need to keep a record of the research and planning you undertake as part of the project. All your results will need to be recorded and any discussions with your teacher or lecturer documented. All this evidence should be recorded.

GRADING

The course assessment is graded A, B, C or D depending on how well you do in the written examination **and** the Project Report, i.e. your total mark out of 130. To gain a course award you must also pass all aspects of the internal assessment.

HOW THIS GUIDE WILL HELP YOU TO MEET THE CHALLENGES

The main aim of this Study Guide is to help you achieve success in the SQA Advanced Higher Chemistry examination by providing you with concise, but comprehensive, coverage of the key areas of the course. Helpful hints and advice are provided in the **Don't forget** sections. The **Things to do and think about** sections provide questions to test your knowledge and understanding of the content and to help you extend your problem-solving skills. In a number of cases, the **Things to do and think about** section provides additional information to extend your knowledge of chemistry and to stimulate your interest in the subject. The **Online tests**, which consist of multiple-choice questions, are a useful tool to check your progress throughout the course and provide relevant feedback. The Study Guide also includes a section offering very useful advice on the production of the Project Report.

DON'T FORGET

The question paper will be set and marked by the SQA.

DON'T FORGET

A Data Booklet containing the relevant data and formulae will be provided.

DON'T FORGET

Internal assessments are set by your school or college following strict criteria given by the SQA.

DON'T FORGET

To gain a course award you will need to pass the internal assessments for all three units, submit a Project Report for external assessment and sit the written examination.

ELECTROMAGNETIC RADIATION AND ATOMIC SPECTRA 1

ELECTROMAGNETIC RADIATION

Chemical reactions take place when the reacting atoms, molecules or ions collide with each other. Therefore the outer electrons are involved when different substances react together and we need to understand the electronic structure of atoms to explain the chemical properties of the elements. Much of the information about the electronic structure of atoms and molecules is obtained using spectroscopic techniques based on different types of electromagnetic radiation.

Electromagnetic radiation includes visible light, microwaves, X-rays and television signals. Electromagnetic radiation can be considered as waves that travel in a vacuum at a constant speed of 3.00×10^8 m s^{-1} with wavelengths between 10^{-14} and 10^4 m.

Different types of electromagnetic radiation make up the electromagnetic spectrum. Visible light – the radiation that our eyes can detect – makes up only a small part of the electromagnetic spectrum.

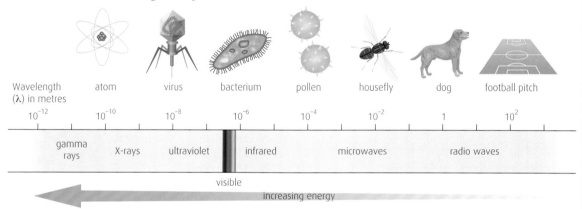

The diagram shows some of the different types of radiation that make up the electromagnetic spectrum. At the high energy end of the spectrum, the waves are so tightly packed that they are closer together than the size of an atom, whereas at the low energy end the waves are further apart than the length of a football pitch.

WAVELENGTH, FREQUENCY AND VELOCITY OF ELECTROMAGNETIC RADIATION

As electromagnetic radiation may be described in terms of waves, it can be specified by its wavelength and/or its frequency.

Wavelength is the distance between adjacent crests or high points of a wave. This distance can be measured in metres. However, in chemistry, the unit of wavelength most often used is the nanometre (nm). One nanometre is 10^{-9} m. The symbol for wavelength is the Greek letter lambda (λ).

Frequency is the number of wavelengths that pass a fixed point in one second. The symbol for frequency is f. Frequency is measured as 1/time and so has units of s^{-1}. This unit is also known as the Hertz (Hz).

All types of electromagnetic radiation travel at the same **velocity** in a vacuum. The velocity is 3.00×10^8 m s^{-1}. This value is given the symbol, c, and it is assumed to be the constant velocity of electromagnetic radiation anywhere.

The relationship between frequency, velocity and wavelength is $f = \frac{c}{\lambda}$.

contd

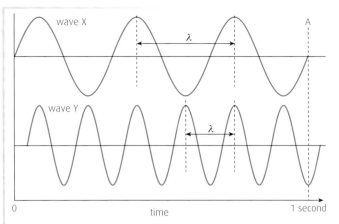

The wavelength of wave X has double the value of the wavelength of wave Y. As both waves travel at the same velocity (c = 3 × 10⁸ m s⁻¹), then twice as many wavelengths of wave Y will pass position A every second compared to wave X. This means that the frequency of wave Y is twice that of wave X.

DUAL NATURE OF ELECTROMAGNETIC RADIATION: WAVES AND PARTICLES

Electromagnetic radiation can be absorbed or emitted. The absorption of ultraviolet radiation by our skin may cause sunburn. When we cook food in a microwave oven, the absorption of microwave radiation by the water in the food causes the water molecules to vibrate, generating heat that cooks the food. However, when electromagnetic radiation is absorbed or emitted by matter, it behaves more like a stream of particles than as a wave motion. These particles are called **photons** and so electromagnetic radiation can be considered both as a stream of photons and as waves with characteristic properties, such as wavelength (λ) and frequency (f). Therefore we say that electromagnetic radiation has a dual nature: wave motion and streams of photons.

Electromagnetic radiation that has a **short wavelength** and **high frequency**, such as gamma rays, is at the **high energy** end of the electromagnetic spectrum.

Radio waves and other radiation with a **long wavelength** and **low frequency** are at the **low energy** end of the electromagnetic spectrum.

When a photon is absorbed or emitted, energy is gained or lost by electrons within the substance. The photons in high frequency radiation transfer greater amounts of energy than photons in low frequency radiation.

This tells us that the energy, E, carried by a photon is related to its frequency. The relationship between energy and frequency is $E = hf$, where h is Planck's constant and has the value $6\cdot63 \times 10^{-34}$ J s. Using this relationship, the energy is calculated in joules (J). In chemistry, energy values are normally expressed in units of kJ mol⁻¹. To convert from J to kJ the number value must be divided by 1000. To obtain mol⁻¹ in units of kJ mol⁻¹, the relationship changes to $E = Lhf$, where L is Avogadro's constant. L has the value $6\cdot02 \times 10^{23}$ mol⁻¹.

Therefore $E = hf$ gives the energy value in J, $E = Lhf$ gives the energy in J mol⁻¹ and $E = \dfrac{Lhf}{1000}$ gives the energy in kJ mol⁻¹.

When the energy is in units of kJ mol⁻¹, this is the energy associated with one mole of photons. Avogadro's constant is the number of formula units in one mole of a substance and so the number of photons in one mole of photons is $6\cdot02 \times 10^{23}$ photons.

It is often useful to relate energy, in kJ mol⁻¹, to wavelength. As $f = \dfrac{c}{\lambda}$, then $E = \dfrac{Lhc}{1000\lambda}$.

DON'T FORGET

The relationship between velocity, frequency and wavelength is $c = f\lambda$. You must be able to use this relationship in calculations.

VIDEO LINK

Watch the video clip on the electromagnetic spectrum at www.brightredbooks.net.

DON'T FORGET

You must be able to use the relationships given on this page.

ONLINE

Values of Planck's constant and Avogadro's constant are given on p. 22 of the SQA Data Booklet. The relationships $c = f\lambda$ and $E = Lhf$ are given on p. 4 of the SQA Data Booklet. The SQA Data Booklet can be downloaded from www.brightredbooks.net

VIDEO LINK

Check out the video clip on the dual nature of electrons at www.brightredbooks.net

ONLINE TEST

Head to www.brightredbooks.net and test yourself on this topic.

THINGS TO DO AND THINK ABOUT

Velocity is measured in m s⁻¹, wavelength is measured in m and frequency is measured in s⁻¹.

When the units are substituted into the equation $c = \lambda f$, the value for c is given in m s⁻¹ and the value for λf is also in m s⁻¹. However, in most chemistry calculations the wavelength is given in nm (10^{-9} m), so you must remember to convert the wavelength from nm into metres by dividing by 10^9 when you are using this equation.

ELECTROMAGNETIC RADIATION AND ATOMIC SPECTRA 2

ATOMIC EMISSION SPECTRA

When white light (such as the light from an ordinary light bulb) is passed through a prism, a rainbow effect is seen. This is known as a continuous spectrum and includes all the colours in the visible part of the electromagnetic spectrum (from about 400 to 700 nm).

When energy in the form of high voltage electricity is passed through a tube of gas, such as hydrogen, at low pressure, coloured light is produced. This light can be analysed by passing it through a prism, diffraction grating or spectroscope. This time, instead of a continuous spectrum, a series of coloured lines is seen. These lines correspond to certain specific frequencies or wavelengths in the visible spectrum. This is known as the atomic emission spectrum for that element. No two elements produce the same atomic emission spectrum. This means that each different chemical element produces its own unique pattern of lines corresponding to different frequencies or wavelengths in its emission spectrum. We can see these lines using a hand-held spectroscope if they occur in the visible part of the electromagnetic spectrum, but if they are outwith the visible spectrum, then we need instruments such as ultraviolet spectrometers to help us 'see' them.

ONLINE

Head to www. brightredbooks.net for more on atomic emission spectra.

WHAT CAUSES ATOMIC EMISSION SPECTRA?

When energy is transferred to atoms, the electrons within these atoms may use this energy to move to higher energy levels. We say that these electrons have become excited. These excited electrons can move back to lower energy levels by losing energy. The energy lost from atoms in this way is released in the form of photons.

Each line in an atomic emission spectrum corresponds to the energy given out when an excited electron moves to a state of lower energy. This can either be to a lower excited state or back to the ground state. Atomic emission spectra provide good evidence for discrete (quantised) energy levels in atoms.

Some atomic emission spectra are shown below:

DON'T FORGET

Each line in an emission spectrum corresponds to the energy given out when an excited electron moves to a lower energy level.

DON'T FORGET

No two elements produce exactly the same emission spectrum.

Hydrogen

Helium

Neon

Sodium

Mercury

THE ATOMIC EMISSION SPECTRUM OF HYDROGEN

There are definite distinct lines in the atomic emission spectrum of hydrogen. These lines are seen in the visible part of the spectrum and there is also a series of lines in the infrared and another series in the ultraviolet part of the electromagnetic spectrum. So, although hydrogen is the simplest element with only one electron per atom, its atomic emission spectrum is fairly complicated.

The different series are shown in the energy level diagram below, which is not drawn to scale. These three series are named after their discoverers. The lines due to excited electrons falling back to the ground state ($n = 1$) are seen in the ultraviolet region. This is because the energy involved corresponds to wavelengths that are shorter than 400 nm.

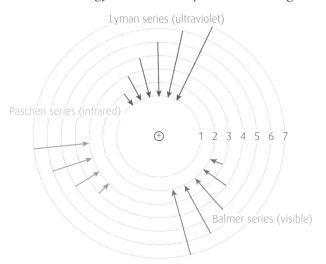

Name of series	Energy level to which the excited electron falls	Where the lines are "seen"
Lyman	$n = 1$	Ultraviolet
Balmer	$n = 2$	Visible
Paschen	$n = 3$	Infrared

These electronic transitions, shown as coloured arrows, correspond to lines with definite values of frequency and wavelength. The diagram is not to scale and the blue lines going back to the ground state should be much longer than the other lines because the difference between the $n = 1$ and $n = 2$ energy levels is by far the greatest, followed by the difference between $n = 2$ and $n = 3$.

Each line in an emission spectrum results from a transition between definite energy levels. Using the frequency or wavelength of each line, it is possible to calculate the energy difference between energy levels.

The structure of the atom as drawn here, with electrons orbiting a central positive nucleus, was proposed by the Danish scientist, Neils Bohr. It worked well for hydrogen, but is not a good model for the atoms of other elements.

DON'T FORGET

The lines in an emission spectrum give information about the difference in energy levels when an excited electron moves to a lower energy level and energy is released.

VIDEO LINK

You can get more information on the atomic emission spectrum of hydrogen by watching the video clips at www.brightredbooks.net

ONLINE TEST

Test yourself on this topic at www.brightredbooks.net

THINGS TO DO AND THINK ABOUT

The energy levels of an atom are closer together the further they are from the nucleus. If you consider the emission spectrum of hydrogen at the high energy or short wavelength end of the spectrum, the lines become increasingly closer until they converge. This is known as the convergence limit. The convergence limit in the Lyman series for hydrogen is at 91·2 nm. You can think of this as the excited electron being at its highest energy level and losing energy as it drops down to the ground state. The highest energy level is as far as the electron can be from the nucleus without being completely removed from the hydrogen atom. Consider this happening in reverse, so that the electron moves from the ground state to just beyond the highest energy level; in this instance, ionisation would have occurred.

Now consider one mole of hydrogen atoms in the gas state forming one mole of hydrogen ions in the gas state. The energy required to do this is the ionisation energy of hydrogen. If you calculate the energy, in kJ mol^{-1}, corresponding to the wavelength of the convergence limit in the Lyman series, you should find that it is almost exactly the same as the value for the ionisation energy of hydrogen given in the SQA Data Booklet. Try this for yourself.

ELECTROMAGNETIC RADIATION AND ATOMIC SPECTRA 3

ATOMIC EMISSION AND ATOMIC ABSORPTION SPECTROSCOPY

Both atomic emission spectroscopy (AES) and atomic absorption spectroscopy (AAS) are used to identify and quantify the elements present in a sample.

Atomic emission spectroscopy is one of the oldest instrumental techniques used for chemical analysis. It is used to study the transitions between electronic energy levels in atoms or ions. These energy differences are usually in the visible region (400–700 nm) of the electromagnetic spectrum, but if the energy difference is larger, then the transitions may lie in the ultraviolet region.

The sample is first converted into a gas and then the electrons are excited by high temperatures from a flame or by using electricity. When the excited electrons fall back to lower energy levels, photons are emitted and electromagnetic radiation of different wavelengths is given out, producing an emission spectrum. By measuring the intensity of the lines at definite wavelengths it is possible to determine not only which elements are present in the sample, but how much of each element is present.

In AAS the electrons are promoted to higher energy levels by absorbing energy, again usually energy corresponding to visible or ultraviolet radiation. An absorption spectrum is produced by measuring how the transmission of light by the sample varies with wavelength. The wavelength of the absorbed light is specific to a particular element and so this technique can be used to determine which elements are present in the sample. The intensity of the absorbed light can also be used to determine the amount of each element in the sample.

The absorption spectrum of an element is the converse of the emission spectrum of that element. This can be seen in the following diagram.

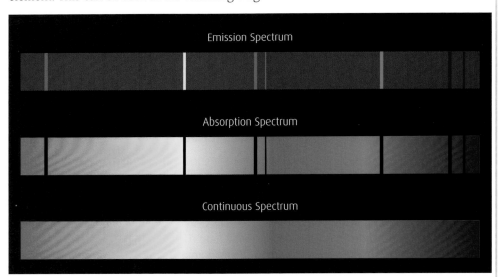

The coloured lines in the emission spectrum are shown as black lines in the absorption spectrum. When the absorption spectrum is superimposed on to the emission spectrum, then a complete continuous spectrum is seen.

DON'T FORGET

Both AES and AAS can be used to identify and quantify the elements present in a sample. AES measures the radiation emitted when excited electrons fall back to lower energy states. AAS measures the absorbed radiation needed to promote electrons to higher energy levels.

DON'T FORGET

Each element has a characteristic absorption and emission spectrum and the **intensity** of the radiation absorbed or emitted is proportional to the concentration of the element present.

USING ATOMIC ABSORPTION SPECTROSCOPY

We can use AAS to determine the amount of metal ions in drinking water or in a variety of foodstuffs, or in the effluent leaving a chemical plant.

A calibration graph is first prepared using samples containing known concentrations of the metal in question. The radiation absorbed by these samples is plotted against the concentration, so when a sample of unknown concentration is analysed by measuring its absorbance, the concentration can be read from the calibration graph. There is more information about calibration graphs in the section on Researching Chemistry.

A typical calibration graph used to measure the concentration of aluminium in drinking water is shown here.

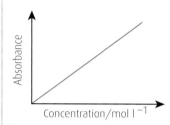

Absorbance values at the wavelength corresponding to aluminium are found using different solutions of known aluminium concentrations. A calibration graph is then plotted. If we measure the absorbance in a sample of drinking water, then the concentration of aluminium corresponding to this absorbance can be read from the calibration graph.

 ONLINE TEST

Head to www. brightredbooks.net and test yourself on electromagnetic radiation and atomic spectra.

 THINGS TO DO AND THINK ABOUT

1   In 1904, Sir William Ramsay was the first Briton to be awarded the Nobel Prize for Chemistry. He was educated at Glasgow Academy and Glasgow University and the prize was in recognition of the work he had carried out with others to discover the noble gases. Helium was discovered in the Sun before it was ever found on planet Earth. How do you think it was possible to do this?

2   The concentration of calcium ions in solution can be determined using an atomic absorption spectrophotometer operating at a wavelength of 422·7 nm. The absorbance was measured for a range of known concentrations of calcium ions and the following calibration graph was drawn.

 ONLINE

You will find more information about Sir William Ramsay and his discoveries at www. brightredbooks.net

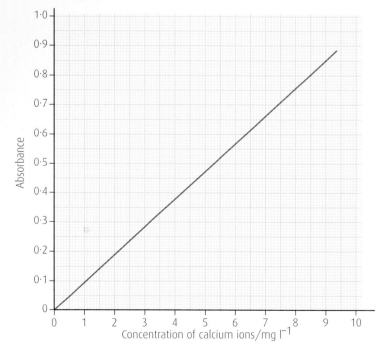

Using this procedure, the absorbance of a sample was found to be 0·38.

Find the concentration of calcium ions in mol l^{-1} in this sample using the calibration graph.

ATOMIC ORBITALS, ELECTRONIC CONFIGURATIONS AND THE PERIODIC TABLE 1

ATOMIC ORBITALS AND QUANTUM NUMBERS

The discrete lines observed in the atomic emission spectra of elements with more than one electron can be explained if electrons, like photons, display the properties of both particles and waves. In the past, scientists considered electrons simply as particles with a negative charge and almost zero mass, but we now think of electrons as having the properties of both waves and particles. For example, in an electron microscope, a beam of electrons of a particular wavelength is fired at the sample to produce an image. This suggests that the beam of electrons is behaving like a beam of light waves.

Electrons within atoms are said to be quantised. This means that they can only possess fixed amounts of energy known as quanta. As a result, electrons can be defined in terms of **quantum numbers**.

Within the atom, electrons behave as waves. Different shapes and sizes of these waves are possible around the nucleus. These are known as 'orbitals'. The simplest orbital is spherical, but more complex orbital shapes are possible. Any orbital, irrespective of its size or shape, can hold a maximum of two electrons.

The **principal quantum number**, n, is related to the size of the orbital. A second quantum number, the **angular momentum quantum number**, l, is used to represent different shapes of orbital. The orientation of any non-spherical orbital is indicated by a third quantum number, the **magnetic quantum number**, m. A fourth quantum number, the **spin quantum number**, s, indicates the spin of an electron within an orbital.

From previous work you already know that electrons are arranged in shells. The shell nearest the nucleus is the first shell and any electron in the first shell has the principal quantum number $n = 1$. Electrons in the second shell have $n = 2$. The higher the value of n, then the further the electrons are from the nucleus.

If the emission spectra of elements other than hydrogen are studied using high resolution spectroscopes, the single lines seen at low resolution often appear as two or three lines very close together. For example, one yellow line is seen in the emission spectrum of sodium at low resolution. However, at higher resolutions it can be seen that there are two lines very close together. This suggests that shells are divided into subshells.

The subshells are labelled s, p, d and f. These letters originally came from old spectroscopic terms 'sharp', 'principal', 'diffuse' and 'fundamental', but these terms are no longer important.

With the exception of hydrogen, the subshells within each shell have slightly different energies: the s subshell has the lowest energy, then p, then d, and so on. The table shows the different subshells present in each shell. Each type of subshell contains one or more **orbitals**.

Shell	Subshell
First	1s
Second	2s, 2p
Third	3s, 3p, 3d
Fourth	4s, 4p, 4d, 4f

Na

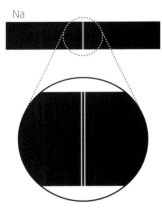

The high resolution emission spectrum of sodium suggests that shells are subdivided into **subshells**. Using quantum mechanics, it can be calculated that all shells have at least one subshell.

NUMBERS AND SHAPES OF ORBITALS

An **s orbital** is spherical like a ball. The s orbital in the first shell is smaller than the s orbital in the second shell. The s orbital in the third shell is bigger than that in the second shell, and so on.

As the first shell has only two electrons, it has only one orbital – the 1s orbital. The second and subsequent shells all have **p orbitals** in addition to an s orbital. The p subshell has three different p orbitals of the same energy. Orbitals that have the same energy are said to be **degenerate**.

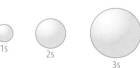

1s   2s   3s

As s orbitals are spherical, they are non-directional.

contd

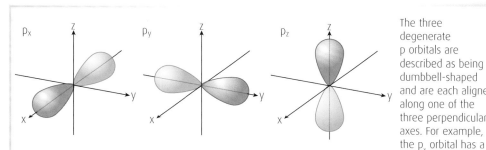

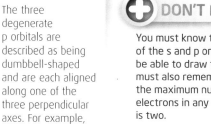

The three degenerate p orbitals are described as being dumbbell-shaped and are each aligned along one of the three perpendicular axes. For example, the p_x orbital has a dumbbell shape and sits on the x-axis.

The second shell can hold a maximum of eight electrons. The s orbital can hold two of these electrons and the three different p orbitals can each hold two electrons. Therefore the second shell has one s and three p orbitals.

The third shell can hold a maximum of 18 electrons. Two of these electrons are in the s orbital and the three p orbitals hold another six electrons. The remaining 10 electrons are accommodated in d orbitals. As an orbital can hold a maximum of two electrons, there must be five d orbitals in the third and subsequent shells.

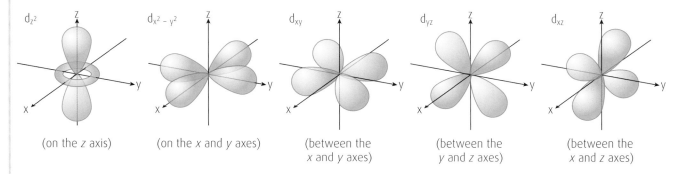

| (on the z axis) | (on the x and y axes) | (between the x and y axes) | (between the y and z axes) | (between the x and z axes) |

These five d orbitals are degenerate with each other, but have higher energies than the s and p orbitals in the same shell. Four of the d orbitals are shaped like a double dumbbell.

THINGS TO DO AND THINK ABOUT

1 The maximum number of electrons in the fourth and subsequent shells is 32. How many electrons will be left after the s, p and d orbitals are filled? These electrons will occupy the f subshell.

   You should be able to calculate the number of f orbitals in the f subshell. Remember that each orbital can hold no more than two electrons. The f orbitals are even more complicated than the d orbitals, but you do not have to know or recognise their shapes.

2 Values of l, the angular momentum quantum number, lie between 0 and $(n - 1)$. The value of l determines the type of orbital. The values of m are from $-l$ through 0 to $+l$. This can be seen in the table.

   If we look at the table closely, we can see that the first shell only has an s orbital. However, the second shell ($n = 2$) has one s orbital ($l = 0$) and three different p orbitals (when $l = 1$, m has three different values).

   The third shell ($n = 3$) has one s orbital, three different p orbitals and five different d orbitals (when $l = 2$, m has five different values).

   Now try to work out the number of s, p, d and f orbitals that can exist in the fourth shell. You could also try to write out the values of n, l, m and s for all the electrons in a completely filled fourth shell.

Value of n	Value of l	Value of m	Type of orbital
1	0	0	s
2	0	0	s
2	1	−1, 0, +1	p
3	0	0	s
3	1	−1, 0, +1	p
3	2	−2, −1, 0, +1, +2	d

ATOMIC ORBITALS, ELECTRONIC CONFIGURATIONS AND THE PERIODIC TABLE 2

DON'T FORGET

Spin quantum numbers have the values $+\frac{1}{2}$ or $-\frac{1}{2}$. If there are two electrons in one orbital, then one has spin quantum number $s = +\frac{1}{2}$ and the other has $s = -\frac{1}{2}$.

PAULI EXCLUSION PRINCIPLE

The **Pauli exclusion principle** states that no two electrons in the same atom can have the same set of four quantum numbers. Put simply, this means that no orbital can hold more than two electrons and the two electrons must have opposite spins. If the two electrons are in one orbital, then both electrons must have the same quantum numbers, n, l and m, but they will have different spin quantum numbers. One will have spin quantum number $s = +\frac{1}{2}$ and the other will have spin quantum number $s = -\frac{1}{2}$.

DON'T FORGET

Degenerate orbitals are orbitals that have the same energy.

AUFBAU PRINCIPLE AND HUND'S RULE

Electrons fill the orbitals in order of increasing energy, meaning that the lowest energy subshells are filled first. This is known as the **aufbau principle**. Of course, some subshells, such as the p subshell and the d subshell, have degenerate orbitals.

Hund's rule states that when degenerate orbitals are available, electrons fill each degenerate orbital singly and with parallel spins, before pairing up to fill the orbitals. To fit with the **Pauli exclusion principle**, two electrons in the same orbital must have opposite spins.

DON'T FORGET

You must know this order. Remember that the 4s orbital has a lower energy than the 3d orbital.

DON'T FORGET

You must know and be able to apply the aufbau principle, Hund's rule and the Pauli exclusion principle.

The orbitals that you need to know, in order of increasing energy, are: 1s, 2s, 2p, 3s, 3p, 4s, 3d, 4p. This is shown diagrammatically in the figure, with boxes representing the orbitals.

ELECTRONIC CONFIGURATIONS USING SPECTROSCOPIC NOTATION

Electronic configurations are similar to electron arrangements. However, electronic configurations show the subshells that the electrons are in, whereas electron arrangements show only the number of electrons in each shell.

For example, lithium has an electron arrangement **2, 1**, but its electronic configuration is $1s^2\ 2s^1$. The characters in **red** indicate the shell and subshell. The numbers in **blue** indicate the number of electrons in that subshell. So the two electrons in the first shell of lithium atoms are located in the 1s subshell or 1s orbital. The one electron in lithium's second shell is in the 2s subshell or 2s orbital. Now consider carbon. It has the electron arrangement **2, 4**. The two electrons in the first shell go into the 1s orbital. The next subshell to be filled is the 2s orbital, which holds a maximum of two electrons. The remaining two electrons go into the next available subshell, which is 2p. So carbon has an electronic configuration $1s^2\ 2s^2\ 2p^2$.

Likewise, the electron arrangement of sodium, **2, 8, 1**, can be written as the electronic configuration $1s^2\ 2s^2\ 2p^6\ 3s^1$. This means that a sodium atom has two electrons in the 1s subshell, two electrons in the 2s subshell, six electrons in the 2p subshell (two electrons in each of the 2p orbitals) and there is one electron in the 3s subshell.

VIDEO LINK

The video clip at www.brightredbooks.net will help you understand the Pauli exclusion principle, the aufbau principle and Hund's rule.

VIDEO LINK

Watch the video clips at www.brightredbooks.net. These will help you understand how to use the Pauli exclusion principle, the aufbau principle and Hund's rule to write electronic configurations of atoms.

THINGS TO DO AND THINK ABOUT

1   An atom of an element has the electronic configuration $1s^2\ 2s^2\ 2p^6\ 3s^2\ 3p^3$. The most likely charge on an ion of this element is:

   A   +5

   B   −1

   C   −2

   D   −3

2   Using spectroscopic notation, write down the electronic configurations of the following species (note that some are ions):

   (a) He; (b) N; (c) Al^{3+}; (d) Ar; (e) Ca; (f) Ca^{2+}; (g) Br^-; (h) S^{2-}

ONLINE TEST

Head to www.brightredbooks.net and take the test on atomic orbitals, electronic configurations and the Periodic Table.

ATOMIC ORBITALS, ELECTRONIC CONFIGURATIONS AND THE PERIODIC TABLE 3

ELECTRONIC CONFIGURATIONS USING ORBITAL BOX NOTATION

Consider the electronic configuration of carbon again: $1s^2\ 2s^2\ 2p^2$. Remember, there are three different p orbitals in the 2p subshell: the p_x orbital lies on the x-axis; the p_y orbital lies on the y-axis and the p_z orbital lies on the z-axis. The different p orbitals are degenerate. To obey Hund's rule, these degenerate orbitals must be filled singly before spin pairing occurs. To obey the Pauli exclusion principle, when an orbital is full with two electrons, these electrons must have opposite spins. This is not shown using spectroscopic notation, but is seen when orbital box notation is used.

Orbital box notation shows the orbitals as boxes with arrows representing electrons. Arrows pointing in the same direction show electrons with the same spin. Electrons with opposite spins are represented by arrows pointing in opposite directions.

The diagram above shows the electronic configuration for carbon in orbital box notation. The two electrons in the p subshell are in different orbitals, but have parallel spins, and the electrons sharing the same orbitals in the 1s and 2s subshells have opposite spins. The diagram also suggests that one of the 2p orbitals is empty. In reality, there is no such thing as an empty orbital. If an orbital is empty, then it does not exist. However, it is acceptable to show 'empty orbitals' in this type of notation.

The electron arrangement of potassium is given in the SQA Data Booklet as 2, 8, 8, 1. In spectroscopic notation, the electronic configuration of potassium is $1s^2\ 2s^2\ 2p^6\ 3s^2\ 3p^6\ 4s^1$. The diagram shows this information presented in orbital box notation.

The electron arrangement of titanium is given in the SQA Data Booklet as 2, 8, 10, 2. In spectroscopic notation, the electronic configuration of titanium is $1s^2\ 2s^2\ 2p^6\ 3s^2\ 3p^6\ 3d^2\ 4s^2$. The diagram shows this information presented in orbital box notation.

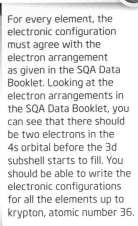

DON'T FORGET

For every element, the electronic configuration must agree with the electron arrangement as given in the SQA Data Booklet. Looking at the electron arrangements in the SQA Data Booklet, you can see that there should be two electrons in the 4s orbital before the 3d subshell starts to fill. You should be able to write the electronic configurations for all the elements up to krypton, atomic number 36.

ONLINE

The aufbau principle and the filling of orbitals is shown at www.brightredbooks.net

IONISATION ENERGIES AND ELECTRONIC CONFIGURATIONS

Look at the graph of the first ionisation energy plotted against atomic number. Ionisation energy is a periodic property. The pattern from Li to Ne is repeated from Na to Ar. In general, the ionisation energy increases across a period. However, there is a decrease from Be to B and from N to O. This is good evidence for the filling of the s and p subshells within the second shell. Likewise, the change in slope from Mg to Al and from P to S provides good evidence for the s and p subshells being filled within the third shell.

contd

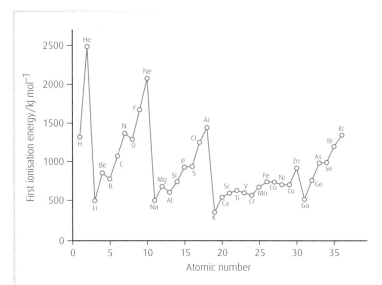

This can be explained in terms of the relative stability of different electronic configurations and thus provides evidence for these electronic configurations. To help you understand this, you have to appreciate that there is a special stability associated with a filled subshell or a half-filled subshell – for example, the p subshell when it contains three or six electrons. Likewise, the d subshell is most stable when it contains five or ten electrons. The more stable the electronic configuration, then the more difficult it is to remove an electron and therefore the ionisation energy is higher.

THE FOUR BLOCKS OF THE PERIODIC TABLE

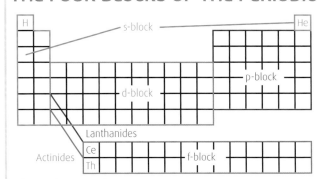

The Periodic Table can be subdivided into four blocks (s, p, d and f). These blocks correspond to the outer electronic configurations of the elements within these blocks.

 THINGS TO DO AND THINK ABOUT

1 According to the aufbau principle, electrons fill orbitals in the order

   A 1s 2s 2p 3s 3p 4s 4p 3d

   B 1s 2s 2p 3s 3d 3p 4s 4p

   C 1s 2s 2p 3s 3p 3d 4s 4p

   D 1s 2s 2p 3s 3p 4s 3d 4p.

2 Using orbital box notation, write down the electronic configurations of the following species (note that some are ions):

   (a) He; (b) N; (c) Al^{3+}; (d) Ar; (e) Ca; (f) Ca^{2+}; (g) Ni; (h) Mn; (i) Br^-; (j) S^{2-}.

3 Explain, in terms of relative stability, why the first ionisation energy of B is less than that of Be and why the first ionisation energy of O is less than that of N.

SHAPES OF MOLECULES AND POLYATOMIC IONS

VSEPR RULES

VSEPR stands for **V**alence **S**hell **E**lectron **P**air **R**epulsion and these electron pair repulsions are responsible for the shapes of molecules and polyatomic ions, such as NH_4^+.

We first calculate the number of outer (or valence) electrons on the central atom of the molecule or ion. This is achieved by taking the number of electrons on the central atom and adding one electron for each of the other atoms attached. If we are dealing with an ion with a +1 charge, we subtract an electron from the total to account for this charge. For an ion with a −1 charge, we add an electron to the total. For example:

BH_3 number of outer electrons on B atom = 3 (from B) + 3 (1 from each H) = 6

NH_4^+ number of outer electrons on N atom = 5 (from N) + 4 (1 from each H) − 1 = 8

AlH_4^- number of outer electrons on Al atom = 3 (from Al) + 4 (1 from each H) + 1 = 8

Dividing the total number of electrons by two gives us the number of electron pairs surrounding the central atom. So BH_3 will have three electron pairs surrounding the central atom, whereas NH_4^+ and AlH_4^- will each have four.

As electron pairs are negatively charged, they will repel each other and will be arranged in such a way as to minimise their repulsion and maximise their separation. Some of the arrangements of electron pairs around the central atom are outlined in the table.

Number of electron pairs	2	3	4	5	6
Shape	Linear	Trigonal planar	Tetrahedral	Trigonal bipyramidal	Octahedral
Angles between electron pairs	180°	120°	109·5°	120° and 90°	90°

SHAPES OF MOLECULES AND IONS

So far we have considered the shapes adopted by electron pairs surrounding the central atom or ion and have taken no account of the two different types of electron pairs – bonding electron pairs and non-bonding electron pairs (lone pairs). The repulsion between the various types of electron pair combinations varies and this can modify the angles between them. Non-bonding pair/non-bonding pair repulsion is greater than non-bonding pair/bonding pair repulsion, which, in turn, is greater than bonding pair/bonding pair repulsion.

The shape of a molecule or ion is governed by the shape adopted by its constituent atoms. In PH_3, for example, there are four electron pairs, but three of them are bonded pairs and one is a non-bonded pair. The four electron pairs adopt a tetrahedral shape but the three bonded pairs adopt a pyramidal shape. So the PH_3 molecule is described as pyramidal, not tetrahedral. As the base of this pyramidal structure is triangular rather than, say, square, the shape is more correctly referred to as **trigonal pyramidal**.

DON'T FORGET

Remember to add one electron if the overall charge is −1 and subtract one electron if the overall charge is +1.

ONLINE TEST

Head to www.brightredbooks.net and take the test on shapes of molecules and polyatomic ions.

DON'T FORGET

The repulsion between non-bonding pairs of electrons is greater than that between bonding pairs of electrons.

VIDEO LINK

Head to www.brightredbooks.net to watch animations showing different shapes of molecules.

EXAMPLES OF MOLECULES WITH DIFFERENT SHAPES

Two bonding pairs: $BeCl_2(g)$

Beryllium is in Group 2 and so has two outer electrons. The two Cl atoms contribute one electron each. This gives four electrons in two electron pairs. As beryllium chloride has two Be–Cl bonds, the two electron pairs are two bonding pairs; there are two bonds around the central beryllium atom. Thus beryllium chloride will be a **linear** molecule, Cl–Be–Cl, with bond angles equal to 180°.

Three bonding pairs: $BCl_3(g)$

Boron is in Group 3 and so has three electrons in the outer shell. The three Cl atoms contribute one electron each, giving a total of six electrons involved in bonding. So there are three B–Cl bonds and no non-bonding pairs on the boron atom. The shape of the boron trichloride molecule will be **trigonal** (or **trigonal planar**) with all four atoms in the same plane.

Four bonding pairs: $CH_4(g)$

In methane, the angle between the bonds is 109·5°. The molecule is a perfect **tetrahedron**.

Four pairs of electrons (three bonding and one lone pair): $NH_3(g)$

Nitrogen has five outer electrons and each hydrogen atom contributes one electron, giving a total of eight electrons (in four pairs) around the N atom. So, in ammonia, there are three N–H bonds and a non-bonding pair of electrons known as a **lone pair**. Repulsion between lone pairs and bonding pairs is greater than between different bonding pairs. The non-bonding pair on the N atom 'squeezes' the three N–H bonds slightly closer together, giving bond angles in NH_3 of 107°, which is slightly less than those in a true tetrahedron.

Four pairs of electrons (two bonding pairs and two non-bonding pairs): H_2O

In water, oxygen has six outer electrons and each hydrogen atom contributes one electron, giving a total of eight electrons around the oxygen atom. There are four electron pairs, but only two O–H bonds; the other electron pairs will be non-bonding or lone pairs. The two non-bonding pairs around the oxygen atom squeeze the two O–H bonds closer together and so the bond angle in H_2O is approximately 104·5°.

Five bonding pairs: $PCl_5(g)$

Phosphorus has five outer electrons and each of the five chlorine atoms contributes one electron, giving a total of 10 electrons (five electron pairs). All the electron pairs are P–Cl bonds. The shape of the molecule is **trigonal bipyramidal**.

Six bonding pairs: $SF_6(g)$

Sulfur has six outer electrons and each of the six fluorine atoms contributes one electron, giving a total of 12 electrons in six electron pairs. All the electron pairs are S–F bonds, so the shape of the molecule is **octahedral**.

Beryllium chloride is linear.

Boron trichloride is trigonal planar.

Methane is a perfect tetrahedron with bond angles of 109·5°.

The bond angles in ammonia are reduced to 107° by the action of a lone pair of electrons.

In water, the action of the two non-bonding pairs reduces the bond angle to 104·5°.

Phosphorus pentachloride is trigonal bipyramidal.

Sulfur hexafluoride is octahedral.

 THINGS TO DO AND THINK ABOUT

Consider the ammonium ion, NH_4^+. Nitrogen has five outer electrons and each hydrogen atom contributes one electron, giving a total of nine electrons. The ammonium ion has a charge of +1, so we must subtract one electron, giving a total of eight electrons and therefore four electron pairs around the central nitrogen atom. These four pairs will all be bonding pairs (there are four N–H bonds in the ammonium ion) and there are no non-bonding pairs. Therefore the shape will be tetrahedral, just like methane.

Calculate the number of bonding and non-bonding electron pairs around the central atom in each of the following species and work out the shape of the molecule or ion:

(a) SiF_4; (b) PCl_3; (c) Cl_2O; (d) ClF_3; (e) I_3^-; (f) IF_5; (g) IF_4^-

DON'T FORGET

To predict the shape of a molecule, you first calculate the number of electron pairs and their arrangement. However, to obtain the actual 'molecular' shape, you must also take into account whether these electron pairs are bonding or non-bonding pairs.

ELECTRONIC CONFIGURATIONS AND OXIDATION STATES OF TRANSITION METALS

ELECTRONIC CONFIGURATIONS

The d block transition metals are metals with an incomplete d subshell in at least one of their ions. We consider the first row of the transition metals as being from scandium to zinc and the second row from yttrium to cadmium. Platinum and gold are in the third row. Most of the common metals in everyday use are transition metals.

When we consider the electronic configurations of the elements from scandium to zinc, we are usually filling the 3d subshell according to the aufbau principle. Once again, the electronic configuration has to fit in with the electron arrangement given in the SQA Data Booklet.

The table shows the electronic configuration in spectroscopic and orbital box notation for the elements from scandium to zinc. [Ar] represents the electronic configuration of argon, which is $1s^2\ 2s^2\ 2p^6\ 3s^2\ 3p^6$. It is okay to use this shorthand here instead of writing out the full electron shells up to 3p. However, in the exam you should write out the spectroscopic notation for each element in full.

DON'T FORGET

Electronic configurations must fit in with the electron arrangements given in the SQA Data Booklet. Remember that the electronic configurations of Cr and Cu are exceptions to the aufbau principle.

Element	Electronic configuration	
	Spectroscopic notation	Orbital box notation (d electrons only)
scandium	[Ar] $3d^1\ 4s^2$	↑ ▯ ▯ ▯ ▯
titanium	[Ar] $3d^2\ 4s^2$	↑ ↑ ▯ ▯ ▯
vanadium	[Ar] $3d^3\ 4s^2$	↑ ↑ ↑ ▯ ▯
chromium	[Ar] $3d^5\ 4s^1$	↑ ↑ ↑ ↑ ↑
manganese	[Ar] $3d^5\ 4s^2$	↑ ↑ ↑ ↑ ↑
iron	[Ar] $3d^6\ 4s^2$	↑↓ ↑ ↑ ↑ ↑
cobalt	[Ar] $3d^7\ 4s^2$	↑↓ ↑↓ ↑ ↑ ↑
nickel	[Ar] $3d^8\ 4s^2$	↑↓ ↑↓ ↑↓ ↑ ↑
copper	[Ar] $3d^{10}\ 4s^1$	↑↓ ↑↓ ↑↓ ↑↓ ↑↓
zinc	[Ar] $3d^{10}\ 4s^2$	↑↓ ↑↓ ↑↓ ↑↓ ↑↓

Chromium and copper

The electron arrangements in the SQA Data Booklet and the electronic configurations written in spectroscopic notation in the table show that chromium and copper are out of step with the aufbau principle. However, there is a special stability associated with half-filled or completely filled d orbitals. Bear this in mind when looking at the orbital box notation and you can understand why chromium is [Ar] $3d^5\ 4s^1$ and copper is [Ar] $3d^{10}\ 4s^1$, rather than the [Ar] $3d^4\ 4s^2$ and [Ar] $3d^9\ 4s^2$ as you might have expected.

DON'T FORGET

When a transition metal atom forms an ion, the 4s electrons are lost before any 3d electrons.

However, when any transition metal atom forms an ion, the electrons that are lost first are those in the outer subshell, the 4s electrons. Therefore the electronic configuration of the Co^{2+} ion is [Ar] $3d^7$.

OXIDATION STATES

The oxidation state is similar to the valency that an element has when it is part of a compound. For example, in iron(II) chloride we might say that the iron has a valency of 2. However, it is actually more accurate to say that iron is in oxidation state (II) or has oxidation number +2.

There are certain rules to be followed when assigning an oxidation number to an element:

- the oxidation number of an **uncombined** element is 0
- for ions containing single atoms such as Na^+ or O^{2-}, the oxidation number is the same as the charge on the ion – in the examples given, these would be +1 and −2
- in most of its compounds, oxygen has oxidation number −2
- in most of its compounds, hydrogen has oxidation number +1
- fluorine has oxidation number −1 in **all** its compounds
- the sum of all the oxidation numbers of all the atoms in a molecule or neutral compound must add up to zero
- the sum of all the oxidation numbers of all the atoms in a polyatomic ion must add up to the charge on the ion

If we want to find the oxidation number of manganese in MnO_4^-, the sum of the oxidation numbers of the one manganese atom and the four oxygen atoms must add up to −1 as this is the charge on the ion. Each oxygen atom has oxidation number −2 and so sum of the oxidation numbers of the four oxygen atoms must be −8. Therefore the oxidation number of manganese must be 7, as 7 − 8 = −1. We can say the manganese has oxidation number +7 or is in oxidation state (VII).

The same transition metal may have different oxidation states in its compounds – for example, you know that the common oxidation states of iron are (II) and (III). In its compounds, copper is usually in oxidation state (II), but it can also have oxidation number +1 in, for example, Cu_2O.

Iron(III) is usually more stable than iron(II); iron(II) compounds in solution are often unstable as they slowly oxidise to iron(III) compounds. Sometimes transition metal compounds have different colours depending on the oxidation state of the metal. For example, iron(II) compounds are often a pale green colour, which slowly changes to the familiar yellow–orange colour of iron(III) compounds as oxidation occurs.

The ion–electron equation for iron(II) ions changing to iron(III) ions is: $Fe^{2+} \rightarrow Fe^{3+} + e^-$

This is a loss of an electron, representing oxidation.

Oxidation can be redefined as an **increase in oxidation number**. **Reduction** can be redefined as a **decrease in oxidation number**.

Oxidising and reducing agents

Acidified permanganate is a very good oxidising agent and the relevant ion–electron equation for this is: $MnO_4^-(aq) + 8H^+(aq) + 5e^- \rightarrow Mn^{2+}(aq) + 4H_2O(l)$

The manganese changes from oxidation state (VII) to oxidation state (II). In general, compounds containing metals in high oxidation states tend to be good oxidising agents as the ions are easily reduced to lower oxidation states. Likewise, compounds containing metals in low oxidation states tend to be reducing agents.

 THINGS TO DO AND THINK ABOUT

1. The d block transition metals are metals with an incomplete d subshell in at least one of their ions. Try to explain why Sc and Zn are often considered **not** to be transition metals.
2. Consider the electronic configurations of the Fe^{2+} and Fe^{3+} ions in both spectroscopic and orbital box notations. Use these notations to explain why Fe(III) compounds are more stable than Fe(II) compounds.
3. Work out the oxidation number of Cr in $Cr_2O_7^{2-}$ (aq) and explain why acidified dichromate is a good oxidising agent.

 ONLINE

You can find more information about calculating oxidation numbers at www.brightredbooks.net

 VIDEO LINK

The video clips at www.brightredbooks.net will teach you more about this topic.

 DON'T FORGET

Oxidation can be considered as an increase in oxidation number and reduction as a decrease in oxidation number.

 ONLINE TEST

Revise your knowledge of this topic by testing yourself at www.brightredbooks.net

TRANSITION METAL COMPLEXES 1

LIGANDS AND COMPLEXES

A **complex** consists of a central metal ion surrounded by ligands. **Ligands** are negative ions or uncharged molecules with one or more non-bonding pairs of electrons (lone pairs). Ligands are electron donors, donating their non-bonding electrons into unfilled metal orbitals and forming what are known as **dative covalent bonds**. A dative covalent bond is one in which both electrons in the bond are donated by one of the atoms, rather than one from each atom. In all other ways, a dative covalent bond is just like any other covalent bond.

Ammonia and water are very common neutral ligands. Ammonia has a non-bonding pair of electrons on the nitrogen atom and water has two non-bonding pairs on the oxygen atom. Common negatively charged ligands include Cl^- and the cyanide ion, CN^-.

DON'T FORGET

Ligands must have at least one non-bonding pair (lone pair) of electrons and these are shown as a pair of dots on the atoms.

Ligands which donate **one pair** of electrons to the central metal ion are said to be **monodentate**. Examples include Cl^- and H_2O. A **bidentate** ligand donates **two pairs** of electrons to the central metal ion. Examples of bidentate ligands include the oxalate ion ($C_2O_4^{2-}$) and 1,2-diaminoethane. They have non-bonding pairs of electrons on the oxygen and nitrogen atoms, respectively.

oxalate ion

1,2-diaminoethane

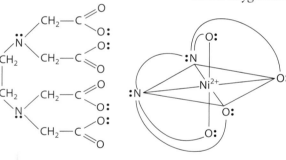

Structure of the EDTA ligand and its complex with the nickel(II) ion.

A **hexadentate** ligand you should be familiar with is ethylenediaminetetraacetic acid (EDTA). It has **six pairs** of non-bonding electrons that bind to a central metal ion in a 1 : 1 ratio. There is more information about EDTA in the Researching Chemistry section. The diagrams show the structure of the EDTA ligand and how it forms a complex with the nickel(II) ion. Note that the EDTA ion has a 4− charge. This is not shown in the diagram; only the non-bonding pairs on the oxygen atoms that form bonds with nickel are shown.

The total number of bonds from the ligand to the central metal ion is known as the **coordination number**. In the Ni^{2+}–EDTA complex, the coordination number is six.

VIDEO LINK

Check out the video clip at www.brightredbooks.net for more on ligands.

NAMING COMPLEXES

Complexes and complex ions are named and written according to rules prepared by the International Union of Pure and Applied Chemistry (IUPAC).

When writing the formula of a complex, the symbol of the metal is written first, then the negatively charged ligands, followed by the neutral ligands. Finally, the formula of the complex ion is enclosed within square brackets as in, for example, $[Fe(OH)_2(H_2O)_6]^+$. This ion has an overall charge of +1 as this is the sum of the Fe^{3+} ion and the two OH^- ions.

Rules for naming complexes are:

- the ligands are named first in alphabetical order, followed by the name of the metal and its oxidation state

- if the ligand is a negative ion ending in –ide, then in the complex the ligand name changes to end in 'o' – examples include chlor**ide**, which becomes **chloro**, and cyan**ide**, which becomes **cyano** and hydrox**ide**, which becomes **hydroxo**.

contd

- if the ligand is ammonia (NH_3), it is named **ammine** in the complex and water as a ligand is called **aqua**

- if carbon monoxide, CO, is the ligand it is called **carbonyl** and the nitrate ion, NO_2^-, is called **nitrito**

- if the complex is a negative ion overall, the name of the complex ion ends in –ate, e.g. cobalt**ate** for a negative ion containing cobalt, **cuprate** is used if the complex contains copper and **ferrate** if it contains iron, from their Latin names (not copperate or ironate)

Examples of names of complexes

- the complex ion $[Cu(H_2O)_4]^{2+}$ is the tetraaquacopper(II) ion

- $[Co(NH_3)_6]^{2+}$ is hexaamminecobalt(II)

- $[Fe(CN)_6]^{4-}$ is hexacyanoferrate(II) as it is a negative ion and the iron is in oxidation state (II)

LOSS OF DEGENERACY AND THE SPECTROCHEMICAL SERIES

In a free transition metal atom or ion (one that is not complexed with any ligands), the five different d orbitals in the 3d subshell are degenerate.

Now consider the formation of an octahedral complex such as $[Ni(H_2O)_6]^{2+}$. Think of six water ligands approaching the Ni^{2+} ion along the x-, y- and z-axes. The electrons in the d orbitals of the nickel ion that lie along the axes will be repelled by the electrons of the approaching ligands.

As a result, these d orbitals now have a higher energy than the d orbitals that lie between the axes. Therefore the d orbitals are no longer degenerate. The d orbitals that lie on the axes are $d_{x^2-y^2}$ (a double dumbbell lying on both the x- and y-axes) and d_{z^2}, which lies on the z-axis. The lower energy orbitals are the d_{xy}, d_{xz}, and d_{yz} orbitals (double dumbbells that lie between the axes).

We call this 'splitting' of the d orbitals. The splitting is different in octahedral complexes compared with tetrahedral and other shapes of complexes.

The energy difference between the different subsets of d orbitals depends on the position of the ligand in the **spectrochemical series**. This is a series that puts in order the ability of different ligands to split the d orbitals. Those ligands that cause a large difference in energy in the d orbitals are said to be 'strong field' ligands, in contrast with 'weak field' ligands where the energy difference is small.

A short form of the spectrochemical series is $CN^- > NH_3 > H_2O > OH^- > F^- > Cl^- > Br^- > I^-$, in which the cyanide ion causes the greatest energy difference.

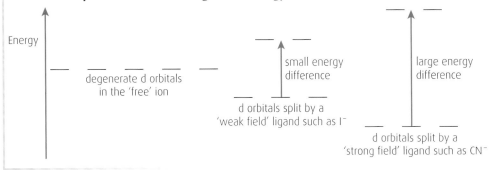

Energy

degenerate d orbitals in the 'free' ion

small energy difference

d orbitals split by a 'weak field' ligand such as I^-

large energy difference

d orbitals split by a 'strong field' ligand such as CN^-

The diagram shows the differing abilities of ligands to split d orbitals; it is a graphical illustration of the spectrochemical series.

 ## THINGS TO DO AND THINK ABOUT

1 Name the following complex ions: (a) $[CoCl_4]^{2-}$; (b) $[Ni(NH_3)_6]^{2+}$; (c) $[PtCl_6]^{2-}$

2 Write the formula for the following complex ions: (a) hexacyanoferrate(III); (b) diamminesilver(I); (c) tetrachlorocuprate(II).

TRANSITION METAL COMPLEXES 2

COLOUR IN TRANSITION METAL COMPLEXES

Many transition metal compounds are coloured. For example, solutions of copper(II) compounds are usually blue and solutions of nickel(II) compounds are usually green. To explain how these colours arise, we must examine simple colour theory.

- white light can be thought of as a combination of three primary colours – red, green and blue
- if red light is absorbed, green and blue light are transmitted and we see this as a blue–green colour, or cyan
- if green light is absorbed, a combination of red and blue light is transmitted and we see this as purple or magenta
- if blue light is absorbed, red and green light are transmitted, which we see as yellow

Why do transition metal compounds absorb light?

Think back to the split d orbitals. Electrons in the lower energy d orbitals can absorb energy and move to the higher energy d orbitals. If the energy absorbed in these so-called d–d transitions is in the visible part of the electromagnetic spectrum, the colour of the transition metal compound will be the complementary colour of the absorbed colour. So the colour we see will be white light minus the colour absorbed.

The colour wheel on p. 20 of the SQA Data Booklet may help you work out which colours are transmitted when any particular colour or wavelength is absorbed.

When the wavelengths of one or more colours are absorbed, the colours on the opposite side of the colour wheel are transmitted.

ULTRAVIOLET AND VISIBLE SPECTROSCOPY

The effects of d–d transitions can be studied using spectroscopy. If the absorbed energy is in the **visible** part of the electromagnetic spectrum, giving a **coloured compound**, visible spectroscopy is used. If the absorbed energy is in the **ultraviolet** part of the electromagnetic spectrum, the compound will be **colourless** and ultraviolet spectroscopy is used.

When the ligands surrounding the transition metal ion are **strong field** ligands such as CN^-, d–d transitions are more likely to occur in the **ultraviolet** region. The wavelength range of ultraviolet light is approximately 200–400 nm.

Complexes containing weak field ligands such as H_2O are more likely to absorb visible light, making them coloured. The wavelength range for the visible region is approximately 400–700 nm.

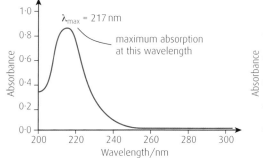

The diagram shows an example of a UV spectrum.

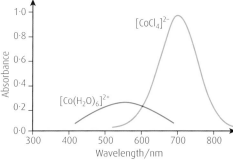

The diagram shows two examples of visible spectra.

A colorimeter fitted with coloured filters corresponding to certain wavelengths in the visible region can be used to measure the absorbance of coloured solutions. A filter of the

ONLINE

You will find more information about using a colour wheel at www. brightredbooks.net

DON'T FORGET

The colour you see is white light minus the colour or colours absorbed. The colour wheel on p. 20 of the SQA Data Booklet may help you.

VIDEO LINK

Check out the video clips at www.brightredbooks.net – these give more information about the spectrochemical series and colour of complexes.

contd

complementary colour to the colour of the solution should be used. You will find more information about using a colorimeter in the Researching Chemistry section.

An ultraviolet spectrometer is a bit more complicated than a colorimeter. Different wavelengths of ultraviolet light from 200 to 400 nm are passed through the sample and the amount of ultraviolet light absorbed at different wavelengths is recorded. The results are plotted automatically as an ultraviolet spectrum. As with a colorimeter, the absorbance is directly proportional to the concentration of the absorbing species.

CATALYSIS

Transition metals and their compounds are used as catalysts. Catalysts you may already know are: iron in the Haber process (industrial production of ammonia); platinum in the Ostwald process (industrial production of nitric acid); and platinum, rhodium and palladium in catalytic converters.

These are all examples of **heterogeneous catalysts** as they are in a different **physical state** to the **reactants** in the reactions being catalysed.

The transition metal atoms or ions on the surface of the active sites of the catalyst form weak bonds with the reactant molecules. It is thought that the presence of unpaired d electrons or unfilled d orbitals allows intermediate complexes to form. The effect of this is to weaken the covalent bonds inside the reactant molecules and, as these reactant molecules are now held in a favourable position, they are more susceptible to attack by molecules of the other reactant. The overall effect is that an alternative reaction pathway with a lower activation energy is provided and so the rate of the reaction is increased.

Another reason that transition metals are good catalysts may be because they have variable oxidation states. Again, this allows the transition metal to provide an alternative reaction pathway with a lower activation energy, so speeding up the reaction.

Cobalt(II) chloride as a catalyst

An experiment you may have carried out in previous years involves the reaction of a solution of potassium sodium tartrate (Rochelle salt) with hydrogen peroxide, which is catalysed by cobalt(II) chloride solution.

The cobalt(II) chloride solution is pink at the start, but during the reaction the pink colour changes to green as Co^{3+} ions form. At this stage there is vigorous effervescence as O_2 gas is given off. At the end of the reaction, Co^{2+} ions are regenerated and the reaction mixture returns to its original pink colour. This is an example of **homogeneous catalysis**.

$$Co^{2+}(aq) \rightarrow Co^{3+}(aq) \rightarrow Co^{2+}(aq)$$

   pink   green   pink

Other examples of homogeneous catalysts include enzymes catalysing reactions in our bodies.

THINGS TO DO AND THINK ABOUT

1. The colours of transition metal compounds are usually explained in terms of d–d transitions, but this is not always the case. For example, the permanganate ion, MnO_4^-, has an intense purple colour. In this ion, manganese is in oxidation state (VII). The electronic configuration of elemental manganese is $[Ar]\ 3d^5\ 4s^2$; the manganese ion in oxidation state (VII) has the electronic configuration $[Ar]$ or $1s^2\ 2s^2\ 2p^6\ 3s^2\ 3p^6$. This means that when manganese is in oxidation state (VII) it has no d electrons, so d–d transitions are not possible. Another transition metal ion that has no d electrons and is coloured is the orange dichromate ion, $Cr_2O_7^{2-}$. Check for yourself that the orange colour of dichromate cannot be a result of d–d transitions.

2. If you look at the example of visible spectra on the opposite page, you will see that both the complex ions contain Co^{2+}, but the peaks of maximum absorbance are at different wavelengths. From the spectra suggest: (i) the colours of these two complex ions and (ii) why the two ions have different peaks of maximum absorbance and different colours. (Hint: explain in terms of splitting of d orbitals.)

ONLINE

You will find more information about ultraviolet and visible spectroscopy at www. brightredbooks.net

ONLINE TEST

Want to revise your knowledge of this topic? Head to www. brightredbooks.net

DON'T FORGET

Transition metals act as catalysts because they have d orbitals available to form intermediate complexes with reactant molecules and because they have variable oxidation states.

ONLINE

You can find more information about transition metals as catalysts at www. brightredbooks.net

VIDEO LINK

Examples of transition metals as catalysts can be seen at www. brightredbooks.net

CHEMICAL EQUILIBRIUM 1: INTRODUCING THE EQUILIBRIUM CONSTANT, K

DON'T FORGET

It is important to appreciate that, when chemical equilibrium has been established, both the forward and reverse reactions continue to take place, but at the same speed.

ONLINE

You can see a fun equilibrium applet at www. brightredbooks.net

DON'T FORGET

You must be able to write the expression for the equilibrium constant for a given equilibrium reaction from a balanced equation.

DON'T FORGET

Equilibrium constants have no units.

DON'T FORGET

The symbol for the equilibrium constant is a capital K

ONLINE

Equilibrium simulations and animations can be found at www.brightredbooks.net

DON'T FORGET

Remember that pure water and solids do not appear in the expression for the equilibrium constant. They are given the value 1.

WHAT IS CHEMICAL EQUILIBRIUM?

A chemical reaction is said to be in dynamic equilibrium, or simply in equilibrium, when the rate of the forward reaction is equal to the rate of the reverse reaction. At equilibrium the concentrations of the reactants and the products will be **constant**, but **not equal**. We can say that the composition of the reactants and products in the equilibrium mixture remains constant indefinitely.

From previous work you should know that the **position of equilibrium** can be changed by

- altering the concentration of a reactant or product
- changing the pressure if there are different numbers of moles of gases on both sides of the balanced equilibrium equation
- altering the temperature

You should also remember that a catalyst speeds up the rate at which equilibrium is reached, but has no effect on the position of equilibrium.

THE EQUILIBRIUM CONSTANT, K

The equilibrium constant has the symbol K and for the general equation aA + bB $\rightleftharpoons$ cC + dD, is given by $K = \dfrac{[C]^c [D]^d}{[A]^a [B]^b}$

where [A], [B], [C] and [D] are the equilibrium concentrations of A, B, C and D, respectively, and a, b, c and d are the stoichiometric coefficients in a balanced reaction equation.

The balanced equation for the Haber process is

$N_2(g) + 3H_2(g) \rightleftharpoons 2NH_3(g)$

and the expression for the equilibrium constant is $K = \dfrac{[NH_3]^2}{[N_2][H_2]^3}$

The concentration values are usually measured in mol l^{-1}, but for gaseous reactions the partial pressures may be used. Whatever the concentrations are measured in, the value calculated for K has **no units**.

The above equilibrium is an example of a homogeneous equilibrium because all the species present at equilibrium are in the same state – in this instance, all the species are gases.

In heterogeneous equilibria, not all the species present are in the same state. An example of a heterogeneous equilibrium reaction is heating calcium carbonate in a closed system so that the carbon dioxide gas produced cannot escape and equilibrium is established. The equation for the reaction is:

$CaCO_3(g) \rightleftharpoons CaO(s) + CO_2(g)$

In a reaction like this, in which a pure solid or solids is present at equilibrium, the concentration of the solid is taken as constant and is given the value of 1 in the expression for the equilibrium constant.

Therefore, in the above equilibrium, instead of $K = \dfrac{[CaO(s)][CO_2(g)]}{[CaCO_3(s)]}$

the correct expression is $K = [CO_2(g)]$.

This is also true for pure liquids; their equilibrium concentration is also given the value 1 in the equilibrium expression. It is not true for aqueous solutions.

Changing the concentration or pressure may affect the position of equilibrium, but it does not affect the equilibrium constant, K. When the concentration (or pressure in

contd

a chemical equilibrium involving gases) is changed, the position of equilibrium also changes until the ratio of the products to reactants returns to its original value – that is, the position of equilibrium changes until the numerical value of K is re-established.

You know from previous work that the presence of a catalyst has no effect on the position of equilibrium. It therefore follows that a catalyst has no effect on the numerical value of the equilibrium constant K.

DON'T FORGET

Changing the concentration (or pressure) or using a catalyst has no effect on the value of K.

EFFECT OF TEMPERATURE ON THE EQUILIBRIUM CONSTANT

The value of the equilibrium constant, K, is dependent on temperature.

Consider the general equation for reactants $\rightleftharpoons$ products.

For an endothermic reaction, an increase in temperature favours the products and so the ratio of [products]/[reactants] increases and therefore K increases. In general, for endothermic reactions, an increase in temperature causes an increase in the yield of the products and the value of K increases.

For an exothermic reaction, an increase in temperature favours the reactants and so the ratio of [products]/[reactants] decreases and therefore K decreases. In general, for exothermic reactions, an increase in temperature causes a decrease in the yield of the products and the value of K decreases.

DON'T FORGET

You must know and understand the effect that changing the temperature has on the value of the equilibrium constant.

ONLINE TEST

Head to www. brightredbooks.net to test your knowledge of chemical equilibrium.

 THINGS TO DO AND THINK ABOUT

Cyclohexane and water do not mix together. We say that they are **immiscible**. Because cyclohexane has a lower density than water, it forms a layer above the aqueous potassium iodide solution when the two are mixed together.

Solid iodine does not dissolve well in water, but will dissolve in aqueous potassium iodide solution and in cyclohexane. If solid iodine is added to a test-tube containing both these immiscible liquids, some of the iodine dissolves in the cyclohexane and the remainder dissolves in the aqueous potassium iodide solution. We say that the iodine **partitions** itself between the two immiscible liquids.

Some of the iodine dissolved in the lower layer starts to move into the upper layer and, at the same time, some of the iodine in the upper layer starts to move into the lower layer. This continues and, when the rate of movement downwards is the same as the rate of movement upwards, a dynamic equilibrium is established.

A particular solute will always partition itself between the same two solvents in the same ratio as long as the temperature is the same. As an equilibrium has been reached, it can be described by an equilibrium constant.

If the equilibrium equation for the process is

$I_2(KI\,(aq)) \rightleftharpoons I_2(C_6H_{12})$ then $K = \dfrac{[I_2(C_6H_{12})]}{[I_2(KI(aq))]}$

This equilibrium constant in partition equilibria is known as the **partition coefficient** and, like all equilibrium constants, it is dependent on temperature. It is not affected by the volume of the solvents or the amount of solute added. However, it does depend on the type of solute and solvent used.

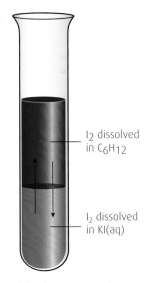

I_2 dissolved in C_6H_{12}

I_2 dissolved in KI(aq)

Solid iodine partitions between two immiscible liquids, cyclohexane and aqueous potassium iodide, until a dynamic equilibrium forms.

1   The equilibrium present in water is given by the equation: $H_2O(l) \rightleftharpoons H^+(aq) + OH^-(aq)$

The value for the equilibrium constant, K, varies with temperature as shown in the table.

a   Write the expression for the equilibrium constant, K.

b   The value of K increases as the temperature increases. What would be the sign of ΔH° for the forward reaction and what type of reaction is it?

Temperature/ °C	Equilibrium constant (K)
0	1.14×10^{-15}
10	2.93×10^{-15}
25	1.01×10^{-14}
50	5.48×10^{-14}

CHEMICAL EQUILIBRIUM 2: K_w AND THE pH SCALE

IONIC PRODUCT OF WATER

In water and all aqueous solutions, some water molecules dissociate or ionise into hydrogen and hydroxide ions. An equilibrium is established between the water molecules and the hydrogen and hydroxide ions.

The ionisation of water can be represented by:
$$H_2O(l) + H_2O(l) \rightleftharpoons H_3O^+(aq) + OH^-(aq)$$

Most hydrogen atoms only contain one proton and one electron. Therefore when the electron is lost, only a proton remains. However, hydrogen ions in water do not exist as free protons, but as hydrated protons. These are given the formula $H_3O^+(aq)$ and are sometimes known as **hydronium ions**.

For simplicity, we often write the above equation as:
$$H_2O(l) \rightleftharpoons H^+(aq) + OH^-(aq)$$

However, you must remember that hydrogen ions in water or in aqueous solution are not free protons, but are hydrated and that $H^+(aq)$ is a shorthand representation of $H_3O^+(aq)$.

The equilibrium constant $K = [H_3O^+(aq)] \times [OH^-(aq)]$ or, more simply, we can write $K_w = [H^+][OH^-]$.

This equilibrium constant or dissociation constant for the ionisation of water is known as the **ionic product** of water and is given the symbol K_w. As K_w is an equilibrium constant, its value is dependent on temperature. At 24°C the value of K_w is approximately 1×10^{-14}.

If we look again at the equation for the ionisation of water, we see that water molecules produce both hydrogen ions, $H_3O^+(aq)$, and hydroxide ions, $OH^-(aq)$. In other words, water is acting as both an acid and as a base. Substances that act as both an acid and a base are called **amphoteric**.

DON'T FORGET

As water is a pure liquid, $[H_2O(l)]$ is given the value 1 and so does not appear in the expression for the equilibrium constant for the ionisation of water.

DON'T FORGET

As K_w is an equilibrium constant, it has no units.

DON'T FORGET

Amphoteric substances such as water can act as both an acid and as a base.

pH SCALE

You already know that:
- acidic solutions have pH values below 7 and $[H^+] > [OH^-]$
- alkaline or basic solutions have pH values above 7 and $[H^+] < [OH^-]$
- neutral solutions have pH = 7 and $[H^+] = [OH^-]$

The greater the concentration of hydrogen ions, the lower the pH value and vice versa. In fact, the relationship between pH and the hydrogen ion concentration is $pH = -\log_{10}[H^+]$ or, if you prefer, this relationship can be written as $[H^+] = 10^{-pH}$.

The pH scale is a logarithmic scale. This means that for a pH change of one unit, the hydrogen ion concentration changes by a factor of 10 and for a pH change of two units, the hydrogen ion concentration changes by a factor of 100, and so on.

The pH of pure water and other neutral solutions can be calculated as follows.

$K_w = [H^+][OH^-] = 1 \times 10^{-14}$. In neutral solutions, $[H^+] = [OH^-]$ and so $K_w = [H^+]^2$. Therefore $[H^+] = \sqrt{(1 \times 10^{-14})} = 1 \times 10^{-7}$ mol l^{-1} and $pH = -\log_{10}[H^+]$ so $pH = -\log(1 \times 10^{-7}) = 7$.

We can use the relationship $[H^+(aq)][OH^-(aq)] = 1 \times 10^{-14}$ to calculate the concentration of hydroxide ions in a solution if we know the concentration of hydrogen ions and vice versa. If the hydrogen ion concentration, $[H^+]$, is known, then the pH can be calculated. This can be seen in the table on page 29. Just as $pH = -\log_{10}[H^+(aq)]$, $pOH = -\log_{10}[OH^-(aq)]$ and a very useful relationship is $pH + pOH = 14$. Note that pH values are not always whole numbers. They can also be non-integral values.

contd

pH	[H⁺(aq)]/mol l⁻¹		[OH⁻(aq)]/mol l⁻¹	pOH
15	1×10^{-15}		1×10^{1} (or 10)	−1
14	1×10^{-14}		1×10^{0} (or 1)	0
13	1×10^{-13}		1×10^{-1}	1
12	1×10^{-12}		1×10^{-2}	2
11	1×10^{-11}		1×10^{-3}	3
10	1×10^{-10}		1×10^{-4}	4
9	1×10^{-9}	Increasing alkalinity	1×10^{-5}	5
8	1×10^{-8}		1×10^{-6}	6
7	1×10^{-7}	Neutral	1×10^{-7}	7
6	1×10^{-6}	Increasing acidity	1×10^{-8}	8
5	1×10^{-5}		1×10^{-9}	9
4	1×10^{-4}		1×10^{-10}	10
3	1×10^{-3}		1×10^{-11}	11
2	1×10^{-2}		1×10^{-12}	12
1	1×10^{-1}		1×10^{-13}	13
0	1×10^{0} (or 1)		1×10^{-14}	14
−1	1×10^{1} (or 10)		1×10^{-15}	15

WORKED EXAMPLES ON pH

1. Calculate the pH of a solution in which the hydrogen ion concentration is 0·38 mol l⁻¹.

$$pH = -\log_{10}[H^+] = -\log_{10}(0\cdot38) = -(-0\cdot42) = \mathbf{0\cdot42}$$

2. Calculate the hydrogen ion concentration in a solution of pH 8·6. This can be done using either of two methods:

(i) $pH = -\log_{10}[H^+]$, so $\log_{10}[H^+] = -8\cdot6$ and therefore $[H^+] = \mathbf{2\cdot51 \times 10^{-9}\ mol\ l^{-1}}$.

(ii) $[H^+] = 10^{-pH} = 10^{-8\cdot6} = \mathbf{2\cdot51 \times 10^{-9}\ mol\ l^{-1}}$.

3. Calculate the pH in a solution in which the hydroxide concentration is $2\cdot4 \times 10^{-4}$ mol⁻¹. This can also be calculated in different ways, but the easiest method is probably:

$$pOH = -\log_{10}[OH^-] = -\log_{10}(2\cdot4 \times 10^{-4}) = -(-3\cdot62) = 3\cdot62$$

$$pH + pOH = 14,\ so\ pH = 14 - pOH = 14 - 3\cdot62 = \mathbf{10\cdot38}$$

THINGS TO DO AND THINK ABOUT

1 A trout fishery added limestone to their loch to combat the effects of acid rain. They managed to increase the pH of the water from 4 to 6. The concentration of H⁺(aq)

    A increased by a factor of 2   C decreased by a factor of 2
    B increased by a factor of 100   D decreased by a factor of 100.

2 A glass of lemon juice was found to have a pH of 3 and a glass of apple juice a pH of 5. From this information, the concentration of hydrogen ions in the lemon juice and apple juice are in the proportion (ratio)

    A 100 : 1   B 1 : 100   C 20 : 1   D 3 : 5.

3 Calculate the pH when the hydrogen ion concentration is: (a) 0·22 mol l⁻¹; (b) $4\cdot1 \times 10^{-6}$ mol l⁻¹; (c) $8\cdot5 \times 10^{-10}$ mol l⁻¹

4 Calculate the hydrogen ion concentration in an aqueous solution which has: (a) pH = 3·2; (b) pH = 9·4; (c) [OH⁻] = $3\cdot9 \times 10^{-9}$ mol l⁻¹; (d) [OH⁻] = $9\cdot4 \times 10^{-7}$ mol l⁻¹

CHEMICAL EQUILIBRIUM 3: THE CONCEPT OF STRONG AND WEAK

STRONG AND WEAK ACIDS

In chemistry, the words **strong** and **weak** have a very different meaning from concentrated and dilute. A strong acid can be either concentrated or dilute depending on the number of moles of acid per litre of solution. The same applies to a weak acid.

A strong acid is completely dissociated (ionised) in aqueous solution.

For example, hydrochloric acid is a strong acid.

An equation showing this is:

$HCl(g) + H_2O(l) \rightarrow H_3O^+(aq) + Cl^-(aq)$

Or, more simply:

$HCl(aq) \rightarrow H^+(aq) + Cl^-(aq)$

An aqueous solution of hydrogen chloride, i.e. hydrochloric acid, will exist entirely as hydrogen ions and chloride ions. No molecules of hydrogen chloride are present. The arrow ($\rightarrow$) tells us that the reaction goes fully in the left to right direction.

Other strong acids include nitric acid and sulfuric acid.

A weak acid is only partially dissociated in aqueous solution.

For example, ethanoic acid is a weak acid. Ethanoic acid has the formula CH_3COOH and a simplified equation showing the dissociation of ethanoic acid is:

$CH_3COOH(aq) \rightleftharpoons CH_3COO^-(aq) + H^+(aq)$

Notice that for ethanoic acid, and any other weak acid, the arrow ($\rightleftharpoons$) tells us that the dissociation is an equilibrium process. The position of the equilibrium lies well over to the left-hand side so there will be very few hydrogen ions and ethanoate ions present at equilibrium compared with the much larger number of ethanoic acid molecules. We can also say that the value of the equilibrium constant, K, for this reaction is much less than 1.

Therefore, because $[H^+(aq)] > [OH^-(aq)]$, ethanoic acid is acidic, but because the position of equilibrium in the dissociation reaction lies well over to the left-hand side, it is much weaker than, say, hydrochloric acid.

All carboxylic acids, such as methanoic acid and propanoic acid , are weak acids. Other weak acids include carbonic acid (an aqueous solution of carbon dioxide) and sulfurous acid (an aqueous solution of sulfur dioxide).

The relevant equations for carbonic acid and sulfurous acid in the SQA Data Booklet are:

$H_2O(l) + CO_2(aq) \rightleftharpoons H^+(aq) + HCO_3^{2-}(aq)$

$H_2SO_3(aq) \rightleftharpoons H^+(aq) + HSO_3^-(aq)$

Note that acids such as sulfuric, carbonic and sulfurous acid, which have two hydrogen atoms per molecule that can become hydrogen ions, are known as diprotic acids. Their ionisation takes place in two steps and this is shown in the SQA Data Booklet (p. 13). Most acids that we cover in this course are **monoprotic**, which means they contain only one hydrogen atom per molecule that can become a hydrogen ion. Hydrochloric, nitric and ethanoic acids are monoprotic acids.

DON'T FORGET

In aqueous solution, strong acids are completely dissociated and weak acids are only partially ionised.

ONLINE

Find out more about comparing strong and weak bases at www.brightredbooks.net

ONLINE

A simple animation on strong and weak acids can be found at www.brightredbooks.net

VIDEO LINK

More information about strong and weak acids can be found at www.brightredbooks.net

STRONG AND WEAK BASES

The same definitions apply to strong and weak bases as to strong and weak acids.

For example, a strong base is completely ionised in aqueous solution, i.e. all the available hydroxide ions are released into solution. Sodium hydroxide is a strong base.

$$Na^+OH^-(s) + H_2O(l) \rightarrow Na^+(aq) + OH^-(aq)$$

A weak base is only partially ionised in aqueous solution. A weak base is made up of molecules. Only some of the molecules are dissociated (ionised) when dissolved in water. Ammonia is a weak base.

$$NH_3(aq) + H_2O(l) \rightleftharpoons NH_4^+(aq) + OH^-(aq)$$

The position of equilibrium lies well over to the left-hand side ($K < 1$) and so, at equilibrium, there will be few ammonium and hydroxide ions compared with the much larger number of ammonia molecules.

Therefore, because $[OH^-(aq)] > [H^+(aq)]$, ammonia is basic, but is weak compared with sodium hydroxide.

Strong bases include the oxides and hydroxides of the alkali metals and also the soluble oxides and hydroxides of the Group 2 metals, such as barium oxide and barium hydroxide.

Weak bases include amines, which you will meet in the Organic Chemistry section. Ethylamine, $C_2H_5NH_2$, is a common amine and the equilibrium present in an aqueous solution of ethylamine is:

$$C_2H_5NH_2(aq) + H_2O(l) \rightleftharpoons C_2H_5NH_3^+(aq) + OH^-(aq)$$

Again, the value of the equilibrium constant, K, is <1 and so the position of equilibrium lies well over to the left-hand side of the equation and ethylamine is a weak base.

 **DON'T FORGET**

You need to know which acids and bases are strong and which are weak.

 VIDEO LINK

The video clip at www.brightredbooks.net covers strong and weak bases.

 THINGS TO DO AND THINK ABOUT

When we say that strong and weak acids do not differ in the stoichiometry of their reactions, we mean that one mole of a weak acid (such as ethanoic acid) reacts in the same molar ratio as one mole of a strong acid (such as hydrochloric acid) when reacting with alkalis, metal oxides, metal carbonates or metals such as magnesium. The molar ratio will be the same, but the reaction rate might be different. This is because, as the hydrogen ions from the weak acid are used up, the weak acid dissociates further to replace these hydrogen ions, so that eventually the weak acid will produce the same number of hydrogen ions as the strong acid.

 ONLINE TEST

Want to revise your knowledge of chemical equilibria? Test yourself at www.brightredbooks.net

1   Which of the following parameters is the same for equal volumes of 0.1 mol l^{-1} solutions of sodium hydroxide and ammonia?

   A   pH of solution
   B   Mass of solute present
   C   Conductivity of solution
   D   Number of moles of hydrochloric acid needed for neutralisation

2   Which of the following statements is true about an aqueous solution of ammonia?

   A   It has a pH less than 7
   B   It is completely ionised
   C   It contains more hydroxide ions than hydrogen ions
   D   It reacts with acids to produce ammonia gas

CHEMICAL EQUILIBRIUM 4: STRONG AND WEAK ACIDS AND BASES AND THEIR SALTS

COMPARING STRONG AND WEAK ACIDS AND STRONG AND WEAK BASES

Solution	pH	Conductivity/siemens
0.10 mol l^{-1} HCl (a strong acid)	1.0	4.1×10^{-2}
0.10 mol l^{-1} CH$_3$COOH (a weak acid)	2.9	2.8×10^{-4}
0.10 mol l^{-1} NaOH (a strong base)	13.0	1.8×10^{-3}
0.10 mol l^{-1} NH$_3$ (a weak base)	10.9	6.2×10^{-5}

Results of tests on 0.1 mol l^{-1} aqueous solutions of strong and weak acids and strong and weak bases are shown in the table.

With the acids, the greater the [H$^+$] then the lower the pH and the greater the conductivity.

With the bases, the greater the [OH$^-$] then the higher the pH and the greater the conductivity.

These experimental results confirm that there are many more hydrogen ions present in a solution of a strong acid than in a weak acid of the same concentration. A further experiment showing this would be adding a piece of magnesium to both acid solutions. Mg reacts with the H$^+$ ions and it reacts much faster with the HCl(aq) than with the CH$_3$COOH(aq) showing again the strong acid contains more ions and that the weak acid is only partially dissociated.

The results in the table also show that there are many more hydroxide ions in a solution of a strong base compared to a weak base of the same concentration.

However if you carry out a titration neutralising, say, 25.0 cm^3 of 0.10 mol l^{-1} NaOH(aq) you would find that 25.0 cm^3 of either 0.10 mol l^{-1} HCl(aq) or 0.10 mol l^{-1} CH$_3$COOH(aq) would be required. We say that strong and weak acids do not differ in the stoichiometry of their reactions. The same is true for strong and weak bases.

pH OF SALT SOLUTIONS

Soluble salts of strong acids and strong bases

A soluble salt of a strong acid and a strong base dissolves in water to form a neutral solution. A good example is sodium chloride (common salt). The parent acid is hydrochloric acid, a strong acid. The parent base is sodium hydroxide, a strong base.

As both the parent acid and the parent base are strong, they are fully ionised in water and the equilibrium present in water is unaffected.

$H_2O(l) \rightleftharpoons H^+ (aq) + OH^-(aq)$

As there are equal numbers of H$^+$ and OH$^-$ ions, the pH of the salt solution is 7.

Soluble salts of strong acids and weak bases

A solution of a salt of a strong acid and a weak base has a pH lower than 7, i.e. it is acidic.

Examples of salts from strong acids and weak bases include ammonium chloride and ammonium nitrate.

Consider a solution of ammonium chloride, $NH_4^+Cl^-$. This is the salt of the strong acid, hydrochloric acid, and the weak base, ammonia.

The equilibrium present in water is:

contd

$$H_2O(l) \rightleftharpoons H^+(aq) + OH^-(aq)$$

Ammonium chloride is acidic in solution and so contains more H^+ than OH^-. This means that some of the OH^- ions present in the water equilibrium must have been removed.

The positive NH_4^+ ions present in ammonium chloride have reacted with the negative OH^- ions to form ammonia molecules. This happens because ammonia is a weak base and, in the equilibrium equation, the position of equilibrium lies well over to the right-hand side, so there will be mainly aqueous ammonia molecules and fewer ions.

$$NH_4^+(aq) + OH^-(aq) \rightleftharpoons NH_3(aq) + H_2O(l)$$

There are now fewer OH^- ions than H^+ ions and this will still be true even when more water molecules dissociate. Therefore the salt solution is acidic.

For any salt of a strong acid and a weak base, $[H^+] > [OH^-]$ and so the solution is acidic.

To explain why it is acidic, we need to work out which ions in the salt have removed some of the OH^- ions from the water. As hydroxide ions are negative, it must be the positive ions from the salt that remove the OH^- ions.

Soluble salts of weak acids and strong bases

A solution of a salt of a weak acid and a strong base has a pH greater than 7, i.e. it is alkaline.

Examples of salts from weak acids and strong bases include sodium ethanoate and potassium carbonate.

Consider a solution of sodium ethanoate, $Na^+CH_3COO^-$. This is the salt of the weak acid, ethanoic acid, and the strong base, sodium hydroxide. Again, the equilibrium present in water is:

$$H_2O(l) \rightleftharpoons H^+(aq) + OH^-(aq)$$

In solution, sodium ethanoate is alkaline and so contains more OH^- ions than H^+ ions. This means that some of the H^+ ions present in the water equilibrium must have been removed.

The negative CH_3COO^- ions present in sodium ethanoate react with the positive H^+ ions to form ethanoic acid molecules. This happens because ethanoic acid is a weak acid and, in the equilibrium equation, the position of equilibrium lies well over to the right-hand side, so there will be mainly aqueous ethanoic acid molecules and fewer ions.

$$CH_3COO^-(aq) + H^+(aq) \rightleftharpoons CH_3COOH(aq)$$

There are now fewer H^+ ions than OH^- ions and this will continue to be true, even when more water molecules dissociate. Therefore the salt solution is alkaline.

For any salt of a weak acid and strong base, $[H^+] < [OH^-]$ and so the solution is alkaline.

To explain why it is alkaline, we need to work out which ions in the salt have removed some of the H^+ ions from the water. As hydrogen ions are positive, it must be the negative ions from the salt that remove the H^+ ions.

pH of soap solution

Soaps are salts of fatty acids (weak acids) and strong bases such as sodium hydroxide or potassium hydroxide. Soaps therefore dissolve in water to form alkaline solutions.

A typical salt is sodium stearate. This is the salt of stearic acid and sodium hydroxide. The formula of stearic acid is $C_{17}H_{35}COOH$ and the formula of sodium stearate is $Na^+C_{17}H_{35}COO^-$.

THINGS TO DO AND THINK ABOUT

1   Propanoic acid can be used to prepare the salt potassium propanoate, CH_3CH_2COOK.

    Explain why potassium propanoate solution has a pH greater than 7. In your answer, you should mention the **two** equilibria involved.

2   Potassium sorbate is a salt used as a preservative in margarine. Potassium sorbate dissolves in water to form an alkaline solution. What does this indicate about sorbic acid?

DON'T FORGET

The pH of a salt solution depends on its parent acid and parent base. If both parents are strong, then the salt solution is neutral. If the parent acid is strong and the parent base is weak, then the salt solution will be acidic. If the parent acid is weak and the parent base is strong, then the salt solution will be alkaline.

ONLINE

A simple simulation of a pH meter used to test the pH of various acidic, alkaline and salt solutions can be found at www.brightredbooks.net

ONLINE TEST

Head to www.brightredbooks.net and take the test on chemical equilibrium.

CHEMICAL EQUILIBRIUM 5: K_a AND THE pH OF WEAK ACIDS

BRØNSTED-LOWRY ACIDS AND BASES

You already know that

- strong acids and strong bases are fully dissociated in aqueous solution
- weak acids and weak bases are only partially dissociated in aqueous solution
- in acidic solutions, $[H^+(aq)] > [OH^-(aq)]$
- in alkaline solutions, $[OH^-(aq)] > [H^+(aq)]$
- hydrogen ions only exist as such when hydrated in aqueous solution and so we usually write their formula as $H^+(aq)$ or $H_3O^+(aq)$
- a hydrogen ion is a hydrogen atom that has lost an electron and so is really just a proton

In 1923, Brønsted and Lowry defined an **acid as a proton donor** and a **base as a proton acceptor**.

When an acid donates a proton, the species that is left is known as the **conjugate base**. For every acid, a conjugate base is formed when the acid loses a proton.

When a base accepts a proton, the species that is left is known as the **conjugate acid**. For every base, a conjugate acid is formed when the base gains a proton (see table for examples).

Acid	Base	Conjugate acid	Conjugate base
HNO_3	H_2O	H_3O^+	NO_3^-
$HCOOH$	H_2O	H_3O^+	$HCOO^-$
H_2O	NH_3	NH_4^+	OH^-
H_2O	$C_2H_5NH_2$	$C_2H_5NH_3^+$	OH^-

When water dissociates into ions, we can write the following equation and identify the conjugate acid and base:

$$H_2O(l) + H_2O(l) \rightleftharpoons H_3O^+(aq) + OH^-(aq)$$

$$\text{acid} + \text{base} \rightleftharpoons \text{conjugate acid} + \text{conjugate base}$$

ACID DISSOCIATION CONSTANT, K_a: CALCULATING THE pH OF A WEAK ACID

For a strong monoprotic acid such as HCl or HNO_3, the hydrogen ion concentration, $[H^+]$, is the same as the concentration of the acid. This is because strong acids fully dissociate, or ionise, in water. This means that all the original acid molecules have changed into ions.

So, in 0·10 mol l^{-1} HCl (aq), $[H^+]$ = 0·10 mol l^{-1}.

However, weak acids are only partially dissociated in aqueous solution. In fact, for most weak acids, less than 1% of the acid molecules become ions in water. This means that, for weak acids, the hydrogen ion concentration, $[H^+]$, is much lower than the concentration of the acid. We therefore need a method to calculate the $[H^+]$ and pH for an aqueous solution of a weak acid.

If we consider any weak acid, such as ethanoic acid, but give it the general formula HA, then the dissociation of the weak acid can be represented by:

$$HA(aq) + H_2O(l) \rightleftharpoons H_3O^+(aq) + A^-(aq)$$

$$\text{acid} + \text{base} \rightleftharpoons \text{conjugate acid} + \text{conjugate base}$$

contd

DON'T FORGET

You must remember these points and also know which acids and bases are strong and which are weak.

DON'T FORGET

You need to know these Brønsted and Lowry definitions of an acid and a base.

VIDEO LINK

You can find some information about the Brønsted-Lowry theory of acids and bases at www.brightredbooks.net

DON'T FORGET

Remember that water is amphoteric, which means it can act as both an acid and a base.

VIDEO LINK

To find out more about conjugate acids and bases, visit www.brightredbooks.net

VIDEO LINK

You will find sample problems on conjugate acid-base pairs at www.brightredbooks.net

This can be written more simply as

$$HA(aq) \rightleftharpoons H^+(aq) + A^-(aq)$$

The equilibrium constant, known as the dissociation constant of the acid, K_a, is given by

$$K_a = \frac{[H^+][A^-]}{[HA]}$$

In a solution of a weak acid, only a very small proportion of the original acid molecules dissociate into ions and therefore [HA] is taken to be the same as the original concentration of the unionised acid molecules and is given the symbol c for concentration.

For every acid molecule that does dissociate into ions, one H^+ ion and one A^- ion will form. Therefore if we ignore any hydrogen ions that come from the water, we can say that

$$[H^+] = [A^-]$$

Therefore

$$K_a = \frac{[H^+]^2}{c}$$

Rearranging this, we can say that, for a weak acid, $[H^+] = \sqrt{K_a c}$, where c is the nominal concentration of the acid.

This enables us to calculate K_a from $[H^+]$ and $[H^+]$ from K_a if the concentration of the weak acid is known.

Just as $pH = -\log_{10}[H^+]$ and $pOH = -\log_{10}[OH^-]$, then the dissociation constant of an acid can be represented by $\mathbf{pK_a = -\log_{10}K_a}$.

It is often more convenient to use pK_a in place of K_a in the same way that it is easier to use pH instead of $[H^+]$.

A very useful expression that allows you to calculate the approximate pH of a **weak** acid from its dissociation constant is

$$\mathbf{pH = \tfrac{1}{2}pK_a - \tfrac{1}{2}\log_{10}c}$$

where c is the nominal concentration of the acid.

These relationships and many others involving pH are given on p. 4 of the SQA Data Booklet.

Values of K_a and pK_a and the relevant equilibrium equations for a variety of weak acids are given on p. 13 of the SQA Data Booklet.

DON'T FORGET

You can find these relationships on p. 4 of the SQA Data Booklet and you must be able to use them in calculations.

DON'T FORGET

You will find values of K_a and pK_a on p. 13 of the SQA Data Booklet.

CALCULATING THE pH OF A WEAK ACID

If you were asked, say, to calculate the pH of a 0.010 mol l^{-1} solution of methanoic acid, you would use the relationship $pH = \tfrac{1}{2}pK_a - \tfrac{1}{2}\log_{10}c$, which is given on p. 4 of the SQA Data Booklet.

The pK_a of methanoic acid is given as 3.75 on p. 13 of the SQA Data Booklet.

So, substituting this value into the equation $pH = \tfrac{1}{2}pK_a - \tfrac{1}{2}\log_{10}c$ gives

$$pH = \tfrac{1}{2}(3.75) - \tfrac{1}{2}\log_{10}0.010 = 1.875 - \tfrac{1}{2}(-2) = \mathbf{2.875} \text{ or } \mathbf{2.88}$$

ONLINE TEST

Test yourself on chemical equilibrium at www.brightredbooks.net

 THINGS TO DO AND THINK ABOUT

1   Write down the equilibrium equations showing the dissociation of the following weak acids: (i) methanoic acid; (ii) ethanoic acid; and (iii) sulfurous acid.

2   Identify the conjugate base and conjugate acid in each of the equilibrium equations you have written in your answers to Question 1.

3   Calculate the pH of: (i) 0.020 mol l^{-1} ethanoic acid; and (ii) 0.0010 mol l^{-1} benzoic acid.

CHEMICAL EQUILIBRIUM 6: BUFFERS AND INDICATORS

DON'T FORGET

The salt of the weak acid provides the conjugate base, which can remove excess hydrogen ions when a small amount of acid is added to a buffer solution.

DON'T FORGET

You need to know what a buffer is and to be able to explain what happens when an acid or a base is added to a buffer solution.

DON'T FORGET

You must be able to calculate the pH of an acid buffer solution.

ONLINE

An animation showing an acid and alkali being added to a buffer can be found at www.brightredbooks.net

ONLINE TEST

A tutorial, another animation, further information and an interesting test on buffers can be found at www.brightredbooks.net

VIDEO LINK

The animation at www.brightredbooks.net uses Lego blocks to explain how a buffer solution works.

BUFFER SOLUTIONS

A buffer solution is one in which the pH remains approximately constant when small amounts of acid or base or water are added.

An acid buffer consists of a solution of a weak acid and one of its salts. An example of an acid buffer is a solution of ethanoic acid and sodium ethanoate. Sodium ethanoate is an ionic salt and, although the sodium ions are just spectator ions, the ethanoate ions are the conjugate base of ethanoic acid. Ethanoic acid is a weak acid and is only partially dissociated:

$$CH_3COOH(aq) \rightleftharpoons CH_3COO^-(aq) + H^+(aq)$$

When an acid is added to this buffer solution, the added H^+ ions from the acid react with the **CH_3COO^- ions from the salt**, forming more undissociated CH_3COOH acid molecules. The overall result is that the concentration of H^+ ions stays the same, so the pH remains unchanged.

When an alkali is added to this buffer solution, the added OH^- ions from the alkali react with the **hydrogen ions from the ethanoic acid**. More ethanoic acid molecules dissociate to replace these hydrogen ions. Again, the overall result is that the concentration of H^+ ions stays the same, so the pH remains unchanged.

A basic buffer consists of a solution of a weak base and one of its salts, such as a solution of ammonia and ammonium chloride. The weak base, ammonia, removes any added hydrogen ions. The conjugate acid, the ammonium ions from the ammonium chloride salt, replaces any hydrogen ions removed when the alkali was added.

The approximate pH of an acid buffer solution can be calculated using the expression

$$\textbf{pH} = \textbf{p}K_a - \textbf{log}_{10} \frac{[\textbf{acid}]}{[\textbf{salt}]}$$

This expression is also given on p. 4 of the SQA Data Booklet.

Using this expression, it is also possible to calculate the required composition of an acid buffer for a certain pH.

CALCULATING THE pH OF A BUFFER SOLUTION

If you were asked, say, to calculate the pH of a buffer solution prepared by mixing 400 cm³ of 0·010 mol l⁻¹ methanoic acid solution with 100 cm³ of 0·050 mol l⁻¹ sodium methanoate solution, you would use the relationship

$$pH = pK_a - \log_{10} \frac{[acid]}{[salt]}$$

The pK_a of methanoic acid given on p. 13 of the SQA Data Booklet is 3·75.

When 400 cm³ of 0·010 mol l⁻¹ methanoic acid is added to 100 cm³ of 0·050 mol l⁻¹ sodium methanoate, both solutions will effectively have been diluted up to 500 cm³ and their concentrations change as follows:

$$[acid] = 0·010 \times \frac{400}{500} = 0·0080 \text{ mol l}^{-1}$$

$$[salt] = 0·050 \times \frac{100}{500} = 0·010 \text{ mol l}^{-1}$$

Putting these values into the expression

$$pH = pK_a - \log_{10} \frac{[acid]}{[salt]}$$

gives

$$pH = 3·75 - \log_{10} \frac{0·0080}{0·010} = 3·75 - \log_{10} 0·80 = 3·75 - (-0·097) = \textbf{3·85}$$

INDICATORS

Indicators are used in acid–base titrations as they change colour at the end-point of the reaction. Indicators are usually weak acids in which the colour of the acid is different from that of its conjugate base. If we represent the indicator as a weak acid of formula HIn, and say it has a red colour, and its conjugate base as In^-, and say it has a blue colour, its dissociation in water can be represented as: $HIn(aq) + H_2O(l) \rightleftharpoons H_3O^+(aq) + In^-(aq)$

Adding an acid (i.e. adding H_3O^+ ions) will shift the position of the equilibrium to the left-hand side and the solution will become red in colour.

Adding an alkali (i.e. adding OH^- ions) will remove hydrogen ions from the equilibrium and the position of the equilibrium will shift to the right-hand side; the colour will now become blue.

For a substance to be a useful indicator, the colour of the non-ionised form, HIn, must be distinctly different from that of its conjugate base, In^-.

The expression for the equilibrium constant for this equilibrium is:

$K_{In} = \dfrac{[H_3O^+(aq)][In^-(aq)]}{[HIn(aq)]}$ which can be rearranged to $\dfrac{[In^-]}{[HIn]} = \dfrac{K_{In}}{[H_3O^+]}$

The colour of the indicator at any time during a titration depends on the relative concentrations of the non-ionised indicator molecules and the conjugate base, i.e. $\dfrac{[In^-]}{[HIn]}$

This will be equal to 1 when $\dfrac{K_{In}}{[H_3O^+]} = 1$, i.e. when $pK_{In} = pH$

This tells us that pK_{In} (the pK of the indicator) is equal to the pH when the indicator changes colour. The colour change is only distinguishable when [HIn] and [In$^-$] differ by a factor of approximately 10 (i.e. only when [HIn] is approximately 10 times greater than [In$^-$], or vice versa). This means that the pH range over which the colour change of the indicator occurs is approximately pH = pKIn ± 1; the approximate range of most indicators is over two pH units.

The pH range of an indicator chosen for a titration must coincide with the point at which the pH is changing very rapidly.

The pH changes during a titration occur most rapidly around the end-point. This is seen in the three diagrams at the side.

To be useful in a titration, the pH range of an indicator must lie within the vertical section of the graph. The pH range of a variety of acid–base indicators is given on p. 20 of the SQA Data Booklet.

THINGS TO DO AND THINK ABOUT

1. **Explain** which of the following indicators could be used to detect the end-point of a titration involving solutions of (a) hydrochloric acid and sodium hydroxide, (b) ethanoic acid and sodium hydroxide and (c) hydrochloric acid and ammonia

   methyl red; phenolphthalein; bromothymol blue; bromocresol purple.

2. What could be added to a solution of propanoic acid to make an acid buffer?

3. Explain how a mixture of solutions of methanoic acid and sodium methanoate act as a buffer when small quantities of (a) HCl(aq) or (b) NaOH(aq) are added.

4. Using information from pp. 4 and 13 in the SQA Data Booklet, calculate the pH of the buffer solution made when 40 cm^3 of 0·1 mol l^{-1} ethanoic acid solution is mixed with 60 cm^3 of 0·1 mol l^{-1} sodium ethanoate solution.

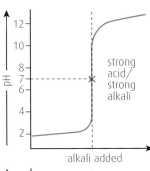

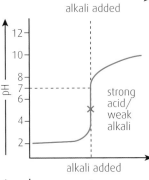

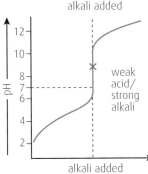

Changes in pH during a titration.

REACTION FEASIBILITY 1

STANDARD ENTHALPY OF FORMATION

We know that the enthalpy change (ΔH) for the reaction R → P is given by: $\Delta H = H_P - H_R$

where H_P and H_R are the enthalpies of the products and reactants, respectively. This expression tells us that ΔH could be calculated if we knew the actual enthalpies of all the reactants and products. However, there is no way that we can determine the **absolute** value of the enthalpy of a substance. Only values relative to an arbitrary reference point can be given and, for all enthalpy expressions, this reference point is called the standard enthalpy of formation. The **standard enthalpy of formation** (ΔH_f°) is defined as the enthalpy change involved when one mole of a substance is formed from its elements in their standard states. The standard state of a substance is its most stable form at a pressure of 1 atm and at a specified temperature, usually taken as 25°C or 298 K.

It follows from the above definition that the standard enthalpy of formation of an element in its most stable form is **zero**.

You will find some standard enthalpies of formation on p. 10 of the SQA Data Booklet.

Now let us consider how the standard enthalpies of formation can be used to calculate the standard enthalpy change for a chemical reaction. First, we calculate the total standard enthalpy of formation of all the products. We then calculate the total standard enthalpy of formation of all the reactants. The difference between the two totals is the standard enthalpy change for the reaction. This is expressed as follows:

$\Delta H^\circ = \Sigma \Delta H_f^\circ$ (products) − $\Sigma \Delta H_f^\circ$ (reactants) where Σ means 'the sum of'.

We will apply this relationship in the following example.

Calculate the standard enthalpy change for the reaction:

$4NH_3(g) + 7O_2(g) \rightarrow 4NO_2(g) + 6H_2O(l)$

given that the standard enthalpies of formation of $NH_3(g)$, $NO_2(g)$ and $H_2O(l)$ are −46, +34 and −286 kJ mol^{-1}, respectively.

$\Delta H^\circ = \Sigma \Delta H_f^\circ$ (products) − $\Sigma \Delta H_f^\circ$ (reactants)

$\qquad = [4(+34) + 6(-286)] - [4(-46) + 7(0)]$

$\qquad = -1396$ kJ mol^{-1}

It is important to remember that the standard enthalpy of formation of each substance has been multiplied by its corresponding stoichiometric coefficient, e.g. the stoichiometric coefficient for $NH_3(g)$ is 4 because there are 4 mol of $NH_3(g)$ in the balanced chemical equation.

DON'T FORGET

The standard state of a substance is its most stable form at a pressure of 1 atm and usually at a temperature of 298 K.

ENTROPY AND ENTROPY CHANGE

The **entropy** of a substance is a measure of the amount of disorder within that system – the larger the value of the entropy, the greater the amount of disorder. Entropy is given the symbol S and the standard entropy of a substance, S°, is the entropy of 1 mol of the substance at a pressure of 1 atm and (usually) a temperature of 298 K. Standard entropy values, S°, for some selected substances are given on p. 17 of the SQA Data Booklet. Notice that the units of entropy are **J K^{-1} mol^{-1}**.

Substances in the solid state tend to have low entropy values. This is not surprising because the particles in a solid occupy approximately fixed positions. They can vibrate, but they cannot move from one place to another. Solids are therefore highly ordered. Gases, however, have very high entropy values. Gases contain particles that have

contd

complete freedom of movement and, as a result, are highly disordered. The entropies of liquids lie between these two extremes.

The graph to the right shows how the entropy of a substance varies with temperature.

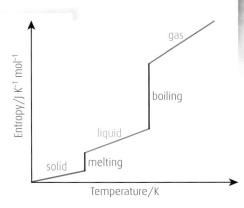

At 0 K, the particles in a solid are no longer vibrating and are perfectly ordered. Therefore the entropy of a substance at 0 K is zero. This is known as the **third law of thermodynamics**. As the temperature increases from 0 K, the entropy of the solid substance increases gradually until its melting point is reached. At this point there is a rapid increase in entropy as the substance changes state from solid to liquid. There is an even larger increase in entropy at the boiling point as the substance changes state from liquid to gas.

So knowing the states of the reactants and products in a chemical reaction should allow us to predict whether the reaction is accompanied by an increase or a decrease in entropy. Consider, for example, the reaction $2Na(s) + Cl_2(g) \rightarrow 2NaCl(s)$. We know that the entropies of solids are very much smaller than the entropies of gases and, because this reaction results in a decrease in the number of moles of gaseous molecules (from 1 to 0), the entropy will decrease. Similarly, we would predict an increase in entropy for the reaction $CaCO_3(s) \rightarrow CaO(s) + CO_2(g)$ because there is an increase in the number of moles of gaseous molecules (from 0 to 1). However, the entropy change for the reaction $CaSiO_3(s) \rightarrow CaO(s) + SiO_2(s)$ is difficult to predict because the reactants and products are solids and are likely to have very similar entropy values. All we can say is that the entropy change is likely to be small.

Changes in entropy have the same sign convention as changes in enthalpy – for increases in entropy, ΔS^o will take a positive sign, i.e. $\Delta S^o > 0$, whereas for decreases in entropy, ΔS^o will take a negative sign, i.e. $\Delta S^o < 0$.

We have seen that by considering the states of the reactants and products in a chemical reaction we can obtain a qualitative idea of the change in entropy but this can be quantified using the expression: $\Delta S^o = \Sigma\ S^o(\text{products}) - \Sigma\ S^o(\text{reactants})$

Consider the following example. Using information from the SQA Data Booklet and the fact that silver(I) nitrate and nitrogen dioxide have S^o values of 142 and 241 J K^{-1} mol^{-1} respectively, calculate the standard entropy change, ΔS^o, for the decomposition of silver(I) nitrate:

$2AgNO_3(s) \rightarrow 2Ag(s) + 2NO_2(g) + O_2(g)$

By substituting in the expression $\Delta S^o = \Sigma\ S^o(\text{products}) - \Sigma\ S^o(\text{reactants})$, we obtain:

$\Delta S^o = [2(43) + 2(241) + (205)] - [2(142)] = +489$ J K^{-1} mol^{-1}

DON'T FORGET

The third law of thermodynamics states that the entropy of a substance at 0 K is zero.

VIDEO LINK

Check out the video clip giving more information on entropy at www.brightredbooks.net

DON'T FORGET

When calculating ΔH^o and ΔS^o values for a reaction, make sure you multiply the standard enthalpy of formation and the standard entropy of each substance by its corresponding stoichiometric coefficient.

ONLINE TEST

Head to www.brightredbooks.net and take the test Reaction feasibility 1.

THINGS TO DO AND THINK ABOUT

1 $2ClF_3(g) + 2NH_3(g) \rightarrow N_2(g) + 6HF(g) + Cl_2(g)$ $\Delta H^o = -1196$ kJ mol^{-1}

   For $NH_3(g)$, $\Delta H_f^o = -46$ kJ mol^{-1} and for HF(g), $\Delta H_f^o = -271$ kJ mol^{-1}

   Using the above information, calculate the standard enthalpy of formation of $ClF_3(g)$.

2 **a** Predict qualitatively the sign of the entropy change expected for each of the following reactions: (i) $I_2(g) \rightarrow 2I(g)$; (ii) $Ag^+(aq) + Cl^-(aq) \rightarrow AgCl(s)$; (iii) $N_2(g) + O_2(g) \rightarrow 2NO(g)$

   b Using information in the SQA Data Booklet and the fact that the standard entropy of NO(g) is 211 J K^{-1} mol^{-1}, calculate the standard entropy change for reaction (iii) in part (a).

REACTION FEASIBILITY 2

FEASIBLE REACTIONS

A **feasible reaction** is one which, if it proceeds, will tend towards the products rather than the reactants. The term feasible, however, tells us nothing about the **rate** at which the reaction takes place.

The **second law of thermodynamics** defines the conditions for a feasible reaction. It states that for a reaction to be feasible, the total entropy change for a reaction system and its surroundings must be positive, that is:

$$\Delta S^\circ_{(total)} = \Delta S^\circ_{(surroundings)} + \Delta S^\circ_{(system)} = + ve$$

Let us consider the feasible reaction: $NH_3(g) + HCl(g) \rightarrow NH_4Cl(s)$

It can be calculated that the standard entropy change for this reaction ($\Delta S^\circ_{(system)}$) is -284 J K^{-1} mol^{-1}. The reaction is exothermic ($\Delta H^\circ = -176$ kJ mol^{-1}) and the heat energy leaving the system increases the entropy of the surroundings. $\Delta S^\circ_{(surroundings)}$ can be calculated using the relationship: $\Delta S^\circ_{(surroundings)} = \dfrac{-\Delta H^\circ}{T}$

where T is the temperature, usually taken as the standard temperature (298 K).

So, $\Delta S^\circ_{(surroundings)} = \dfrac{-\Delta H^\circ}{T} = \dfrac{-(-176)}{298} = 0.591$ kJ K^{-1} mol^{-1} = $+591$ J K^{-1} mol^{-1}

Hence, $\Delta S^\circ_{(total)} = \Delta S^\circ_{(surroundings)} + \Delta S^\circ_{(system)} = (+591) + (-284) = +307$ J K^{-1} mol^{-1}

The overall entropy change is positive, which confirms that the reaction is feasible.

DON'T FORGET

For a reaction to be feasible, the total entropy must increase.

FREE ENERGY

So far we have used $\Delta S^\circ_{(total)}$ to predict the feasibility of a reaction. However, it is more convenient to introduce another property known as the **standard free energy change**, ΔG°, to do the same. It focuses on the reaction system itself and is defined as:

$$\Delta G^\circ = \Delta H^\circ - T\Delta S^\circ$$

For a reaction to be feasible, ΔG° must be negative, i.e. $\Delta G^\circ < 0$. This is just another way of stating the second law of thermodynamics.

Let us apply this expression to determine whether the following reaction is feasible:

$2NaHCO_3(s) \rightarrow Na_2CO_3(s) + CO_2(g) + H_2O(g)$

For this reaction, $\Delta H^\circ = +129$ kJ mol^{-1} and $\Delta S^\circ = +335$ J K^{-1} mol^{-1} or $+0.335$ kJ K^{-1} mol^{-1}.

Hence at standard temperature (298 K), $\Delta G^\circ = +129 - 298(0.335) = +29$ kJ mol^{-1}.

Since ΔG° is positive, it can be concluded that the reaction is not feasible at 298 K.

A reaction is feasible when ΔG° is negative and so a reaction will just become feasible when $\Delta G^\circ = 0$.

DON'T FORGET

It is important to remember in calculating ΔG° that the units of ΔS° are kJ K^{-1} mol^{-1} in order to match up with those of ΔH° (kJ mol^{-1}).

Substituting $\Delta G^\circ = 0$ in the above expression gives $0 = \Delta H^\circ - T\Delta S^\circ$, which can be rearranged to $T = \dfrac{\Delta H^\circ}{\Delta S^\circ}$

So the decomposition of sodium hydrogencarbonate just becomes feasible at

$T = \dfrac{129}{0.335} = 385$ K

This means that the reaction is feasible at all temperatures above 385 K, but it is not feasible at temperatures below 385 K.

Just as the standard enthalpy change for a reaction can be calculated from the standard enthalpies of formation of the reactants and products, the standard free energy

contd

change (ΔG°) for a reaction can be calculated from the standard free energies of formation (ΔG°_f) of the reactants and products using the following expression:

$$\Delta G^\circ = \Sigma\, \Delta G^\circ_f \text{ (products)} - \Sigma\, \Delta G^\circ_f \text{ (reactants)}$$

The standard free energy of formation of an element in its most stable form is always zero, just like the standard enthalpy of formation of an element.

FREE ENERGY AND EQUILIBRIUM

Consider the reversible reaction $\mathbf{R} \rightleftharpoons \mathbf{P}$.

ΔG° for this reaction is given by $G^\circ_P - G^\circ_R$, where G°_P and G°_R are the standard free energies of the products and reactants, respectively. Let us assume that ΔG° for this reaction is negative.

If we start with 1 mol of pure **R** at 1 atm pressure, then standard state conditions apply and so, just before the reaction starts, we can talk about the standard free energy of **R** (G°_R) as opposed to the free energy of **R** (G_R). However, as soon as the reaction starts and some **R** is converted into **P**, standard state conditions no longer apply. Therefore during a chemical reaction we must talk about free energy (G) rather than the standard free energy (G°). As this reaction approaches equilibrium, the free energy of the system proceeds to a minimum, as illustrated in the diagram. You can see that the products predominate over the reactants, so the equilibrium position lies on the product side.

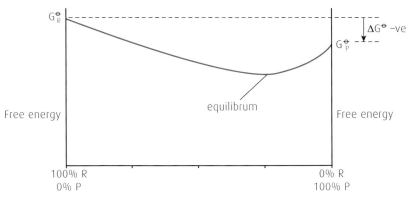

When equilibrium is established, the free energy of **R** will equal that of **P** and so:

$$\Delta G = G_P - G_R = 0$$

It is important to note that, at equilibrium, $\Delta G = 0$ and **not** $\Delta G^\circ = 0$.

We have shown that standard free energy change (ΔG°) for a reaction can give information about the equilibrium position in a reversible reaction.

In summary, if:

- $\Delta G^\circ < 0$, the forward reaction will be feasible and the products will predominate over the reactants. In other words, the equilibrium position will lie to the side of the products and K, the equilibrium constant will be greater than 1.

- $\Delta G^\circ > 0$, the reverse reaction will be feasible and so the reactants will predominate over the products. It follows that the equilibrium position will lie to the side of the reactants and K will be less than 1.

No matter how fast or slow a feasible reaction takes place, the concentration of products will always be greater than the concentration of the reactants once equilibrium is established.

 THINGS TO DO AND THINK ABOUT

The graph above shows the variation in free energy for the reversible reaction $R \rightleftharpoons P$. Use this graph to calculate an approximate value for K, the equilibrium constant for the reaction.

 **DON'T FORGET**

When a reversible reaction reaches a state of equilibrium, $\Delta G = 0$.

 VIDEO LINK

Head to www. brightredbooks.net and watch the video clip giving an overview of the second law of thermodynamics.

 ONLINE TEST

Test yourself on Reaction feasibility 2 at www. brightredbooks.net

KINETICS

RATE EQUATION, ORDER OF REACTION AND RATE CONSTANT

The rate of a chemical reaction normally depends on the concentrations of the reactants. Consider the reaction $A + B \rightarrow$ products

Suppose, when the initial concentration of **A** is doubled and the initial concentration of **B** is kept constant, the rate of the reaction doubles. This implies that the rate of reaction is directly proportional to the concentration of **A**, so rate $\propto [A]^1$.

Suppose, also, that the rate increases by a factor of four when the initial concentration of **B** is doubled and that of **A** is kept constant. This implies that the rate is directly proportional to the square of the concentration of **B**, so rate $\propto [B]^2$.

Combining these results gives rate $\propto [A]^1[B]^2 = k[A]^1[B]^2$ ....(1)

where k is a constant. We say that the reaction is first order with respect to **A** and second order with respect to **B**.

In general, for a reaction of the type $aA + bB \rightarrow$ products, the dependence of the rate on the concentrations of **A** and **B** may be expressed as rate $= k[A]^m[B]^n$

An expression of this kind is known as the **rate equation** for the reaction. The indices, m and n, are the orders of the reaction with respect to **A** and **B**, respectively, and you will notice that they bear no relation to the stoichiometric coefficients a and b. The reaction is said to be m order with respect to **A** and n order with respect to **B**. The orders, m and n, are usually small whole numbers (including zero) and are rarely greater than two.

The **overall order of the reaction** is given by (m + n). For example, in the reaction described by rate equation (1) above, the overall order would be (1 + 2) = 3.

The constant k in the rate equation is known as the **rate constant** and the units of the rate constant vary depending on the overall order of the reaction. Suppose that a reaction is third order overall. Its rate equation could take the form rate $= k[A]^1[B]^2$

Rearranging this expression gives $k = \dfrac{\text{rate}}{[A]^1[B]^2}$

The rate is normally measured in mol l^{-1} s^{-1} and the units of concentration are mol l^{-1}, so the units of k for this third order reaction are $\dfrac{\text{mol l}^{-1}\text{s}^{-1}}{(\text{mol l}^{-1})\,(\text{mol}^2\,\text{l}^{-2})} = \text{mol}^{-2}\,\text{l}^2\,\text{s}^{-1}$.

Rate constant units for zero to third order reactions are summarised in the table on the left.

The rate equation for a chemical reaction can only be derived experimentally. Normally, a series of experiments in which the initial concentrations of the reactants are varied is carried out and the initial rate of reaction in each experiment is determined.

Consider the experimental data for the reaction: $A + B + C \rightarrow$ products.

By comparing experiments 1 and 2, you can see that doubling the concentration of A increases the reaction rate by a factor of two, which implies the reaction is first order with respect to A.

By comparing experiments 1 and 3, you can see that doubling the concentration of B has no effect on the rate. This means the reaction is zero order with respect to B.

By comparing experiments 1 and 4, you can see that doubling the concentration of C increases the reaction rate by a factor of four, implying that the reaction is second order with respect to C.

DON'T FORGET

There is no relation between the orders of reaction and the stoichiometric coefficients.

Overall order	Units of k
0	mol l^{-1} s^{-1}
1	s^{-1}
2	mol^{-1} l s^{-1}
3	mol^{-2} l^2 s^{-1}

Experiment	[A]/ mol l^{-1}	[B]/ mol l^{-1}	[C]/ mol l^{-1}	Initial rate/ mol l^{-1} min^{-1}
1	1·0	1·0	1·0	0·20
2	2·0	1·0	1·0	0·40
3	1·0	2·0	1·0	0·20
4	1·0	1·0	2·0	0·80

contd

The rate equation is therefore rate = $k[A]^1[B]^0[C]^2$ or, more simply, rate = $k[A]^1[C]^2$

The reaction is third order overall.

The rate constant can be determined by substituting experimental data from any one of the four experiments into the rearranged rate equation. If we take the data from experiment 1:

$$k = \frac{rate}{[A]^2[C]^2} = \frac{0.20}{(1.0) \times (1.0)^2} = 0.20 \text{ mol}^{-2} \text{ l}^2 \text{ min}^{-1}$$

DON'T FORGET

The order and rate equation for a chemical reaction can only be determined from experimental results.

REACTION MECHANISMS

Most reactions are believed to proceed by a series of steps rather than by one single step. This series of steps is known as the **reaction mechanism**. The slowest step in the reaction mechanism is called the **rate-determining step** and it governs the overall rate of the reaction.

Once the kinetics of a reaction have been worked out, it is possible to propose a mechanism for the reaction. Consider, for example, the reaction between nitrogen dioxide and fluorine. The stoichiometric equation for the reaction is $2NO_2 + F_2 \rightarrow 2NO_2F$

and the experimentally determined rate equation is rate = $k[NO_2][F_2]$

We can see that the reaction is **first** order with respect to each of the reactants and this tells us that **one** molecule of NO_2 and **one** molecule of F_2 must be involved in the slow, rate-determining step. The following reaction mechanism can be proposed:

Step 1 $NO_2 + F_2 \rightarrow X$ slow   Step 2 $NO_2 + X \rightarrow 2NO_2F$ fast

It has been shown from additional experimental evidence that intermediate X is a mixture of NO_2F and F. The mechanism for the reaction is therefore:

Step 1 $NO_2 + F_2 \rightarrow NO_2F + F$ slow   Step 2 $NO_2 + NO_2F + F \rightarrow 2NO_2F$ fast

Adding the two steps together gives: $2NO_2 + F_2 \rightarrow 2NO_2F$, which is identical to the stoichiometric equation for the reaction. This must be the case for the mechanism to be valid.

You will come across reaction mechanisms again on pp. 58, 59, 64 and 65.

DON'T FORGET

A rate equation can only tell us which species react together in the rate-determining step and how many particles of each are involved in that step.

VIDEO LINK

Watch the video clip giving an overview of reaction kinetics at www.brightredbooks.net

ONLINE TEST

Test yourself on kinetics at www.brightredbooks.net

THINGS TO DO AND THINK ABOUT

1   For the reaction $CH_3Br + OH^- \rightarrow CH_3OH + Br^-$, the experimentally determined rate equation is rate = $k[CH_3Br][OH^-]$.

The table shows some kinetic data for this reaction.

Experiment	[CH₃Br]/mol l⁻¹	[OH⁻]/mol l⁻¹	Relative rate
1	0.05	0.10	1
2	0.05	0.20	*x*
3	0.10	*y*	10

Determine values for **x** and **y**.

2   The rate equation for a reaction between P and Q is rate = $k[P]^2[Q]$

Calculate the factor by which the rate of the reaction will increase if the concentration of P is doubled and that of Q is trebled.

3   The reaction $A + 2B \rightarrow 2C + D$, is thought to proceed by the following mechanism:

Step 1: $A + B \rightarrow C + X$ slow   Step 2: $X + B \rightarrow C + D$ fast

Deduce the orders of the reaction with respect to A and B and then write the rate equation for the reaction.

MOLECULAR STRUCTURE

REPRESENTATIONS OF ORGANIC COMPOUNDS

There are various ways of representing organic compounds and, as these are universal, chemists the world over can communicate with each other, despite the fact that they may speak different languages. We will consider these different representations in the following sections.

Empirical and molecular formulae

The simplest formula for an organic compound is called its **empirical formula**. This shows the elements present in the compound and the simplest ratio of the atoms of these elements in the compound. For example, ethane (C_2H_6) has an empirical formula of CH_3, whereas benzene (C_6H_6) has an empirical formula of CH. Empirical formulae can be determined by a technique known as elemental microanalysis and you will find out more about this on p. 72.

The **molecular formula** of a compound shows the actual number of each kind of atom present in a molecule of the compound. To work out the molecular formula of a compound, we need to know both the empirical formula and the relative molecular mass of the compound. The latter can be determined by mass spectrometry (see p. 73).

Suppose we have a compound with the empirical formula CH_2O and a relative molecular mass of 60. The relative empirical mass will be $[12 + 2(1) + 16] = 30$, which is half the relative molecular mass. This implies that the molecular formula must be twice the empirical formula, i.e. $2 \times (CH_2O) = C_2H_4O_2$.

> **DON'T FORGET**
>
> The molecular formula of an organic compound gives the number of each kind of atom present in a molecule of the compound. It must never show the functional groups.

Full and abbreviated structural formulae

The **structural formula** of a compound not only shows the number of each kind of atom in the molecule, but also how the atoms are joined together. The simplest of these structural formulae is the **full structural formula**, in which all the bonds between the atoms are displayed. For example, the full structural formula of 2,3-dimethylpentan-3-ol is drawn on the left and alongside it are two **abbreviated structural formulae**.

$CH_3CH(CH_3)C(CH_3)(OH)CH_2CH_3$

full structural formula

abbreviated structural formulae

The first of the abbreviated structural formulae has the formula condensed on to one line. These formulae can be difficult to write, particularly for branched molecules. As you can see, the second abbreviated structural formula shows all the carbon-to-carbon bonds and the branches can be clearly seen. If you are asked to draw an abbreviated structural formula, then it is advisable to use the second of these two types.

Skeletal structural formulae

The ultimate abbreviation of organic structures uses lines to represent the carbon framework. In these so-called **skeletal structural formulae**, each line is understood to have a carbon atom at each end unless another atom, such as oxygen or nitrogen, is attached. Consider 2,3-dimethylpentan-3-ol again. By redrawing the second of its abbreviated formulae with a zigzag arrangement of the bonds, you can see that is fairly straightforward to derive its skeletal structure.

It is important to note that, in a skeletal structural formula, the carbon atoms are not shown and neither are the hydrogen atoms attached to the carbon atoms. Hydrogen atoms are only shown if they are bonded to atoms such as oxygen or nitrogen.

abbreviated structure

skeletal structure

contd

The table shows further examples of skeletal structural formulae.

Skeletal structural formulae are commonly used, particularly for large molecules, because they are easily drawn and the functional groups are clearly shown.

Name	Abbreviated structure	Skeletal structure
Butane	$CH_3CH_2CH_2CH_3$	 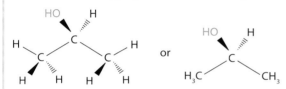
Propene	$CH_3CH=CH_2$	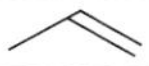
Propanoic acid	CH_3CH_2COOH	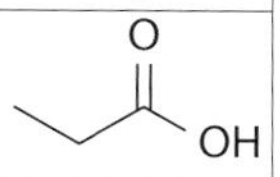
2-Methylbutanal	$CH_3CH_2CH(CH_3)CHO$	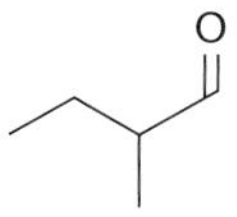

Three-dimensional representations

Organic molecules are three-dimensional, so showing structures on paper in two dimensions can give a misleading picture of what the molecule actually looks like. This has led to the use of wedged line notation, which provides a simple way of showing organic molecules to indicate their three-dimensional nature.

We can apply this notation to monochloromethane (CH_3Cl):

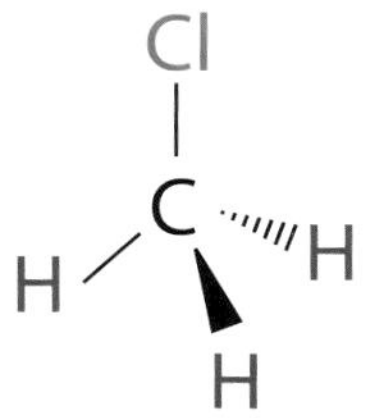

The plain lines represent bonds that lie in the plane of the paper. The full wedge represents a bond coming out of the paper and the hashed wedge indicates a bond pointing behind the paper.

In a similar fashion, propan-2-ol could be represented as:

There are various molecular drawing packages available. One of these is ChemSketch and it is free to download from the internet.

THINGS TO DO AND THINK ABOUT

1   The skeletal structural formula of aspirin is shown here.

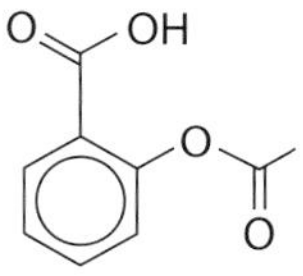

   a   Write the molecular formula of aspirin.
   b   Write the empirical formula of aspirin.

2   Draw a skeletal structural formula for each of the following compounds:

   a   methanoic acid
   b   butanone
   c $(CH_3)_2NH$
   d   Cl
       $CH_3CHCHOH$
           CH_3

   e $(CH_3)_3CCOOCH_2CH_3$

   f $CH_3CH=CHCH(CH_3)_2$

3   Convert each of the following skeletal structural formulae into an abbreviated structural formula:

   a   **b**   **c** 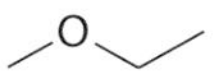   **d**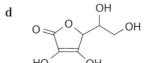

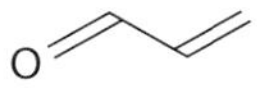

DON'T FORGET

In skeletal structural formulae, carbon atoms are not shown and hydrogen atoms are only shown if they are bonded to atoms other than carbon.

DON'T FORGET

You must be able to draw full structural formulae, abbreviated structural formulae and skeletal structural formulae and be able to interconvert them.

VIDEO LINK

For a tutorial on drawing skeletal structures, visit www.brightredbooks.net

ONLINE

You will find a very useful resource explaining how to use ChemSketch at www.brightredbooks.net

ONLINE TEST

Test your knowledge of molecular structure at www.brightredbooks.net

MOLECULAR ORBITALS 1

FORMATION OF MOLECULAR ORBITALS

Chemical bonding can be described in terms of a **molecular orbital model**. The molecular orbital approach is based on the idea that, as electrons in **atoms** occupy **atomic orbitals**, electrons in **molecules** occupy **molecular orbitals**. Molecular orbitals have many of the same properties as atomic orbitals. They are populated by electrons, beginning with the orbital with the lowest energy and a molecular orbital is full when it contains two electrons of opposite spin.

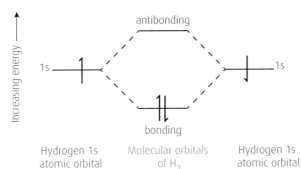

Hydrogen 1s atomic orbital   Molecular orbitals of H_2 Hydrogen 1s atomic orbital

Molecular orbitals are generated by combining atomic orbitals. The number of molecular orbitals formed is always equal to the number of atomic orbitals that combine. So, if two atomic orbitals combine, then two molecular orbitals will be formed. This is the case when two hydrogen 1s atomic orbitals combine to produce two molecular orbitals in a hydrogen molecule (H_2).

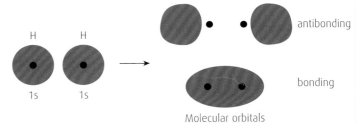

Molecular orbitals

The diagram on the left shows that one of the molecular orbitals is lower in energy than either of the two atomic orbitals that combined to produce it. This is called a **bonding molecular orbital**. The other molecular orbital is known as an **antibonding molecular orbital** and it is of higher energy than either of the atomic orbitals that combined to produce it. The H_2 molecule has only two electrons and both occupy the bonding molecular orbital; the antibonding molecular orbital is empty. The other diagram shows the shapes of the two molecular orbitals. You can see that the bonding molecular orbital embraces both nuclei, unlike the antibonding molecular orbital. In general, the attraction of the positively charged nuclei to the negatively charged electrons occupying the bonding molecular orbital is the basis of bonding between atoms.

DON'T FORGET

When two atomic orbitals combine, two molecular orbitals (one bonding and the other antibonding) are formed.

SIGMA AND PI BONDS

The formation of **bonding** molecular orbitals by an overlap of atomic orbitals applies not only to the 1s orbitals of hydrogen, but also to other atomic orbitals. When the atomic orbitals overlap along the axis of the bond, a covalent bond, called a **sigma** (σ) bond, results. This is normally referred to as **'end-on' overlap**. Some examples of the formation of σ bonds from overlapping atomic orbitals are shown in the diagrams.

Overlap of two 1s orbitals   Overlap of a 1s orbital and a 2p orbital   Overlap of two 2p orbitals

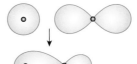
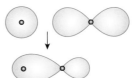
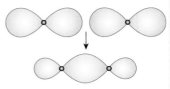

As you have already seen, a σ bond of this type is present in an H–H molecule.

A σ bond of this type is present in an H–F molecule.

A σ bond of this type is present in an F–F molecule.

contd

Consider now the overlap of two parallel p atomic orbitals that lie perpendicular to the axis of the bond:

The atomic orbitals overlap laterally or 'side-on' and form a **pi (π) bond**.

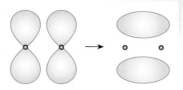

π bonds arise when atoms form multiple bonds. The double bond in an oxygen molecule, for example, comprises one σ bond and one π bond, while the triple bond in a nitrogen molecule is made up of one σ bond and two π bonds. Side-on overlap of atomic orbitals is much less efficient than end-on overlap and, as a consequence, π **bonds are weaker than σ bonds**. This is borne out by the fact that a carbon-to-carbon double bond is not twice as strong as a carbon-to-carbon single bond (see p. 10 of the SQA Data Booklet).

Formation of a π bond.

DON'T FORGET

Sigma (σ) bonds are formed by the end-on overlap of atomic orbitals and π bonds result from side-on overlap.

HYBRIDISATION

Carbon is the basis of all organic compounds and forms four covalent bonds. In many of these, the arrangement of the four bonds around the carbon atom is tetrahedral.

In its ground state, a carbon atom has the electronic configuration $1s^2\ 2s^2\ 2p^2$, which, in orbital box notation is:

As you can see, carbon has two half-filled orbitals in the 2p subshell and, at first sight, it might have been expected to form two covalent bonds rather than the four. So why does carbon form four covalent bonds?

Carbon has one empty 2p orbital and so we can obtain more half-filled orbitals by promoting one of the paired 2s electrons into this empty 2p orbital:

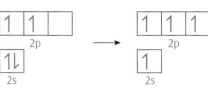

The carbon atom now has four unpaired electrons and can form four bonds, but we still have not explained why these bonds adopt a tetrahedral arrangement. To do this, we introduce the concept of hybridisation. **Hybridisation** is the process of mixing atomic orbitals within an atom to generate a set of new atomic orbitals called **hybrid orbitals**. In the case of a carbon atom, the **one** 2s orbital can mix with the **three** 2p orbitals to form **four** hybrid orbitals known as sp^3 **hybrid orbitals**.

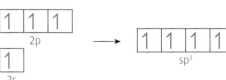

The four sp^3 hybrid orbitals are degenerate and, as they are identical in shape, they will point towards the corners of a tetrahedron to minimise repulsion.

It is important to note that sp^3 hybridisation is not the only type of hybridisation shown by carbon (see p. 48), nor is hybridisation limited to carbon.

It is also important to appreciate that the number of hybrid orbitals formed is always equal to the number of atomic orbitals that were mixed.

DON'T FORGET

Hybridisation is the process of mixing atomic orbitals within an atom to form a set of degenerate hybrid orbitals.

THINGS TO DO AND THINK ABOUT

1   Quinoline has the following structure:

State the number of (a) σ bonds and (b) π bonds in a molecule of quinolone. (Hint: drawing the full structural formula of quinoline will help.)

2   In iodine heptafluoride, IF_7, the iodine atom uses sp^3d^3 hybrid orbitals.

State the number and type of atomic orbitals that mix to form the set of sp^3d^3 hybrid orbitals.

VIDEO LINK

For an overview of σ bonding, π bonding and hybridisation, visit www.brightredbooks.net

ONLINE TEST

Test your knowledge of molecular orbitals 1 at www.brightredbooks.net

MOLECULAR ORBITALS 2

DON'T FORGET

The bonding in ethane can be explained in terms of **sp^3 hybridisation** and σ **bonds.**

BONDING IN ALKANES

We have already explained, in terms of hybridisation, how a carbon atom can form four sp^3 hybrid orbitals (see p. 47). We can apply this concept to explain the bonding in alkanes. Ethane is taken as an example of a typical alkane. The four sp^3 hybrid orbitals on each carbon atom will overlap end-on with four other orbitals: three hydrogen 1s orbitals and one sp^3 hybrid orbital on the other carbon atom. Four σ bonds will be formed and they will adopt a tetrahedral arrangement. This is illustrated for ethane in the diagram.

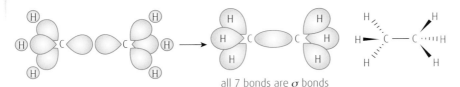

all 7 bonds are σ bonds

Notice that all seven covalent bonds in an ethane molecule are σ bonds.

BONDING IN ALKENES

All alkenes contain a carbon-to-carbon double bond. We can use ethene as a typical example to explain the bonding in alkenes. On each carbon atom of the double bond, the 2s orbital mixes with two of the 2p orbitals to form three degenerate sp^2 hybrid orbitals. The remaining 2p orbital is left unhybridised.

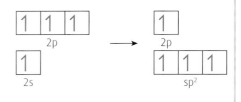

To minimise repulsion, the three sp^2 hybrid orbitals adopt a trigonal planar arrangement, i.e. they lie in the same plane with an angle of 120° between them.

Each carbon atom in ethene uses its three sp^2 hybrid orbitals to form σ bonds with two hydrogen atoms and with the other carbon atom. The unhybridised 2p orbitals left on the carbon atoms overlap side-on to form a π bond. The formation of the bonds in ethene is illustrated in the following diagram.

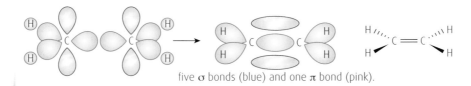

five σ bonds (blue) and one π bond (pink).

Of the six bonds in ethene, five are σ bonds (shown in blue) and one is a π bond (shown in pink).

Although both carbon atoms in ethene are sp^2 hybridised, this is not true for all the carbon atoms in **alkenes**. In propene ($CH_3CH{=}CH_2$), for example, only the two carbon atoms of the double bond are sp^2 hybridised – the third carbon atom is sp^3 hybridised.

DON'T FORGET

The bonding in ethene can be explained in terms of **sp^2 hybridisation** and σ and π **bonds**.

THE BONDING CONTINUUM

We know that the three types of chemical bonds that exist between atoms are non-polar covalent bonds, polar covalent bonds and ionic bonds. We are already familiar with the idea that it is helpful to think of these as making up a **bonding continuum**. Non-polar covalent bonding lies at one end of the continuum and ionic bonding at the other; polar covalent bonding lies between these two extremes.

In **non-polar covalent bonds**, the bonding electrons are shared equally between the two atoms of the bond. Such bonds exist between two identical atoms and between two atoms of different elements with the same electronegativity values.

contd

In **polar covalent bonds**, the bonding electrons are shared unequally, with the atom with the larger value of electronegativity having the greater share of the electrons. This atom will carry a partial negative charge ($\delta-$), leaving the atom with the smaller value of electronegativity carrying a partial positive charge ($\delta+$). Although the atoms in polar covalent bonds do not have fully-fledged charges like the ions in ionic compounds, these partial charges imply that polar covalent bonds have some ionic character. It follows that the more polar the covalent bond, the greater the ionic character.

In **ionic bonds**, the bonding electrons have been transferred from one atom to the other, resulting in the formation of ions. In most ionic compounds, the bonding electrons are not completely transferred and this implies some degree of electron sharing, i.e. covalent character. In general, ionic bonds are formed between atoms with very large differences in electronegativity. However, the smaller this difference, the more covalent the character of the ionic bond.

These three different types of bonding can also be described in terms of **molecular orbitals**.

The bonding molecular orbital in a **non-polar covalent bond** is completely symmetrical about the midpoint between the two atoms of the bond.

The bonding molecular orbital in a **polar covalent bond**, however, is asymmetrical about the midpoint between the two atoms. It is skewed towards the atom with the greater electronegativity.

An **ionic bond** is an extreme form of polar covalent bonding. We can still regard the bonding pair of electrons as occupying a molecular orbital, but an orbital that embraces only one atom of the bond. This is an extreme case of asymmetry where an electron has been effectively stripped from one atom and transferred to the other, resulting in the formation of ions.

Summary of different types of bonding.

non-polar covalent bonding	polar covalent bonding	ionic bonding

| bonding electrons **shared equally** between two atoms | bonding electrons **shared unequally** between two atoms | bonding electrons **transferred** from one atom to the other |

ionic character increasing

covalent character decreasing →

Bonding molecular orbital in a non-polar covalent bond.

Bonding molecular orbital in a polar covalent bond.

Bonding molecular orbital in an ionic bond.

THINGS TO DO AND THINK ABOUT

As well as exhibiting sp³ and sp² hybridisation, carbon can also be **sp** hybridised. Here, the 2s orbital mixes with one of the 2p orbitals to generate two degenerate sp hybrid orbitals. The remaining two 2p orbitals are left unhybridised.

To minimise repulsion, the angle between the two sp hybrid orbitals will be 180°. We can consider ethyne (C_2H_2), in which both carbon atoms are sp hybridised. Each carbon atom uses its two sp hybrid orbitals to form σ bonds with a hydrogen atom and with the other carbon atom. The unhybridised 2p orbitals left on the carbon atoms overlap side-on to form **two** π bonds.

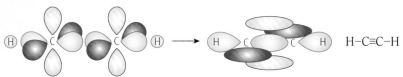

So, in ethyne, there are three σ bonds and two π bonds.

The concept of sp hybridisation can be used to explain the bonding in other molecules, for example, nitrogen.

DON'T FORGET

The bonding molecular orbital is symmetrical in a non-polar covalent bond, but asymmetrical in polar covalent and ionic bonds.

ONLINE

A PowerPoint presentation covering molecular orbitals, hybridisation and the bonding continuum can be downloaded from www.brightredbooks.net

ONLINE TEST

Test your knowledge of molecular orbitals 2 at www.brightredbooks.net

MOLECULAR ORBITALS 3

MOLECULES AND COLOUR

In the inorganic section we looked at transition metal compounds that are coloured as a result of the absorption of visible light. The absorption of visible light by these compounds results in electrons moving from a low energy state to a higher energy state. The colour of the compound is seen as the complementary colour to the light absorbed.

Organic compounds also absorb electromagnetic energy. Most organic compounds are colourless because the wavelength of light absorbed does not lie in the visible range of the electromagnetic spectrum. However, there are some organic compounds that are coloured. To explain this, we need to consider the arrangement of electrons in an organic molecule.

MOLECULAR ORBITALS AND ORGANIC COMPOUNDS

As we have already seen, two molecular orbitals form when two atomic orbitals overlap – a bonding molecular orbital and an antibonding molecular orbital. End-on overlap of atomic orbitals along the axis of the bond results in σ and σ^* molecular orbitals forming. Side-on overlap of atomic orbitals at an angle perpendicular to the axis of the bond results in the formation of π and π^* molecular orbitals.

Electrons fill the bonding molecular orbitals first as they have a lower energy than the antibonding molecular orbitals. So, under normal conditions, the antibonding molecular orbitals will be empty. The orbital containing the electrons with the highest energy is known as the **H**ighest **O**ccupied **M**olecular **O**rbital (**HOMO**). The name given to the lowest energy molecular orbital that is empty is the **L**owest **U**noccupied **M**olecular **O**rbital (**LUMO**).

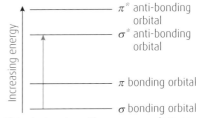

This electron transition corresponds to an electron moving from the HOMO to LUMO in a simple organic molecule containing only carbon-to-carbon single bonds.

In organic molecules containing only carbon-to-carbon single bonds and with no non-bonding electrons, the HOMO is the σ bonding orbital and the LUMO is the σ^* antibonding molecular orbital. The energy gap between the HOMO and the LUMO is large and corresponds to ultraviolet light. No visible light is absorbed and so these compounds are colourless. Even simple molecules with π bonds are colourless as the energy gap between the π bonding molecular orbital (HOMO) and the σ^* antibonding molecular orbital (LUMO) is still too large for visible light to be absorbed.

COLOURED ORGANIC COMPOUNDS

The photographs show the structures of coloured organic compounds.

A pair of jeans with an overlay of the structure of indigo dye.

Purple wool with an overlay of the structure of the dye.

Carrots with an overlay of the structure of the coloured component.

contd

DON'T FORGET

White light can be thought of as a combination of three primary colours: red, green and blue.

DON'T FORGET

When two atomic orbitals overlap end-on along the axis of the bond, a σ molecular orbital forms. Atomic orbitals that overlap side-on form π molecular orbitals.

VIDEO LINK

Check out the video clip at www.brightredbooks.net for more on this.

ONLINE TEST

Test your knowledge of conjugated systems at www.brightredbooks.net

You will see that all of these coloured molecules have similar structural features: relatively large numbers of carbon atoms and multiple double bonds or benzene rings. These features allow the molecule to have electrons that are delocalised across a number of carbon atoms. This is known as a **conjugated system**. An organic molecule must contain a large degree of conjugation to be coloured.

Consider the two molecules on the right. Molecule **A** has a system of alternating double and single bonds and so is a conjugated molecule. Molecule **B** does not have a conjugated system.

molecule **A**

molecule **B**

For a molecule to have a conjugated system, it must contain a chain of alternating σ and π bonds or benzene rings that allow electrons to be delocalised across a number of carbon atoms. For further information about delocalisation in benzene rings, see p. 68.

see p. 68.

CONJUGATION AND CHROMOPHORES

The table gives information about two coloured molecules.

Compound	Structure	Number of C=C in conjugated system	Colour of compound
Vitamin A	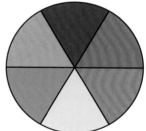	5	Yellow
β-Carotene	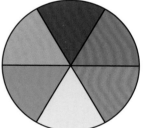	11	Orange

The number of carbon-to-carbon bonds within the conjugated system affects the colour of the compound. The colour arises as electrons absorb energy and move from the HOMO to the LUMO. The colour of the compound is the colour complementary to that absorbed.

A simple colour wheel can be used to predict colours. Colours that are opposite each other on the wheel are complementary, e.g. purple is complementary to yellow.

The information in the table suggests that vitamin A absorbs visible light of a greater energy (smaller wavelength) than β-carotene. As it appears yellow, vitamin A must be absorbing purple light (approximately 410 nm). For β-carotene to appear orange, it must be absorbing blue light (approximately 480 nm). We can also see that the degree of conjugation in β-carotene is greater than that in vitamin A. The greater the degree of conjugation in a molecule, the smaller the HOMO–LUMO energy gap and therefore the lower the absorbed energy.

The word **chromophore** is used to describe the group of atoms within a molecule responsible for the absorption of light in the visible region of the electromagnetic spectrum.

ONLINE

Learn more by following the link at www.brightredbooks.net

DON'T FORGET

The SQA Data Booklet contains a colour wheel that you can use to work out complementary colours.

A simple colour wheel.

DON'T FORGET

The greater the degree of conjugation within a molecule, the smaller the energy gap between the HOMO and the LUMO and so light of a longer wavelength (lower energy) will be absorbed.

THINGS TO DO AND THINK ABOUT

We saw earlier that molecules **X** and **Y**, shown on the right, gave rise to the indigo colour of blue jeans and the purple colour of wool, respectively.

molecule **X**

molecule **Y**

a   Explain how the colour arises in these molecules.

b   What colour of light is being absorbed in (i) molecule **X** and (ii) molecule **Y**? What does the colour of molecule **X** tell you about the HOMO–LUMO energy gap compared with that in molecule **Y**?

DON'T FORGET

A coloured organic molecule will contain a conjugated system that allows electrons to be delocalised across a number of carbon atoms. Chromophores are often systems containing alternating single and double bonds. Molecules containing benzene rings can also be chromophores.

STEREOCHEMISTRY

STEREOISOMERISM

Molecules that have the same molecular formula but differ in the way their atoms are arranged are called **isomers**. They are distinct compounds, often with different physical and chemical properties.

There are two ways in which atoms can be arranged differently in isomers:

* the atoms are bonded together in a different order in each isomer – these are called **structural isomers**
* the order of bonding in the atoms is the same, but the arrangement of the atoms in space is different for each isomer – these are called **stereoisomers**

You have already covered **structural isomerism** in earlier work and we will now explore **stereoisomerism**. There are two types of stereoisomerism: **geometric isomerism** and **optical isomerism**.

GEOMETRIC ISOMERISM

cis-but-2-ene

trans-but-2-ene

Geometric isomers of but-2-ene; *cis* means 'on the same side' and you can see that in *cis*-but-2-ene both methyl groups lie on the same side of the double bond. *Trans* means 'on different sides' and so in *trans*-but-2-ene the methyl groups are on different sides of the double bond.

To illustrate what is meant by geometric isomerism, we will consider the alkene but-2-ene (H_3C–HC=CH–CH_3). It contains a carbon-to-carbon double bond and the diagrams on the left show the spatial arrangement of the bonds around each carbon atom. Furthermore, this arrangement of atoms and bonds is planar and all the bond angles around the C=C double bond are 120°. The bonds are fixed in relation to one another. This means that it is impossible to rotate one end of an alkene molecule around the C=C double bond while the other end is fixed. This is one of the reasons why some alkenes can exhibit geometric isomerism.

Returning to our example, you will find that there are two geometric isomers of but-2-ene. One is referred to as the **cis isomer** and the other is the **trans isomer**. It is important to remember that geometric isomers are different compounds and have distinct physical properties. For example, *cis*-but-2-ene melts at −139°C, whereas *trans*-but-2-ene melts at −105°C.

But-2-enedioic acid also has *cis* and *trans* forms. As well as differing in their physical properties, *cis*-but-2-enedioic acid and *trans*-but-2-enedioic acid also differ in one of their chemical properties.

cis-but-2-enedioic acid   *trans*-but-2-enedioic acid

Cis-but-2-enedioic acid is readily dehydrated to form a cyclic anhydride. However, as the carboxyl groups are on opposite sides of the C=C double bond in the *trans* isomer, they are not in a suitable orientation to undergo such a reaction.

In the *cis* isomer the carboxyl groups are in the correct orientation to allow this dehydration to proceed; in the *trans* isomer they are not.

So, geometric isomerism can occur in organic compounds that contain a C=C double bond. However, in addition to the double bond, the molecule must have two different groups attached to each of the carbon atoms of the double bond. Propene, for example, would not exhibit geometric isomerism because it has two identical hydrogen atoms attached to one of the carbon atoms of the double bond.

Geometric isomerism can arise as a result of a lack of free rotation around a bond, often a carbon-to-carbon double bond.

Although geometric isomerism is most common in compounds containing a C=C double bond, it can also arise in saturated rings where rotation about the C–C single bonds is restricted.

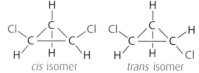

cis isomer   *trans* isomer

1,2-Dichlorocyclopropane has these two geometric isomers.

OPTICAL ISOMERISM

To illustrate what is meant by optical isomerism, consider lactic acid (2-hydroxypropanoic acid). It contains a tetrahedral carbon atom (shown in black) with **four different groups** attached. As a result, lactic acid exists as two distinct isomeric forms.

Each isomer is the **mirror image** of the other and they are known as **optical isomers** or **enantiomers**. But all molecules have mirror images, yet they do not all exhibit optical isomerism. What makes lactic acid different is that its two isomers are **non-superimposable**. You should make molecular models of these optical isomers to convince yourself that one isomer cannot be superimposed on the other.

In general, if a molecule contains a tetrahedral carbon atom that has four different groups attached to it, then it will have an optical isomer. These molecules can be described as **chiral**. You are already familiar with chiral objects in everyday life, such as hands, feet and so on.

The two optical isomers of lactic acid.

Plane-polarised light

Optical isomers are identical in every physical property except their effect on plane-polarised light. A beam of light consists of an infinite number of waves vibrating in all planes perpendicular to the direction in which the light travels. If this beam of light is passed through a polariser (such as the Polaroid film in Polaroid sunglasses), all the vibrations are cut out except those in one plane. The light emerging from the polariser is plane-polarised light.

When plane-polarised light is passed through a solution containing one optical isomer, the plane of the polarised light is rotated through a certain angle. If this solution is replaced by an equimolar (same concentration) solution of the other optical isomer, it too rotates the plane of polarised light by exactly the same angle, but in the opposite direction. For example, if one isomer of an optically active compound rotates the plane of polarised light by +50° in a clockwise direction, the other optical isomer will rotate it by −50° in an anticlockwise direction, provided that the concentrations of the two solutions are equal. An equimolar mixture of the two optical isomers would have no effect on plane-polarised light because the rotational effect of one would be cancelled out by the opposite rotational effect of the other. Such a mixture is **optically inactive** and is known as a **racemic mixture**.

Many of the organic compounds found in nature are chiral. More importantly, most natural compounds in living organisms are not only chiral, but are present in only one of their optical isomeric forms. Such compounds include amino acids, proteins, enzymes and sugars.

THINGS TO DO AND THINK ABOUT

You may have heard of the **thalidomide** tragedy. Thalidomide was widely prescribed to pregnant women in the 1950s and early 1960s as a drug to combat morning sickness. Tragically, many of the babies born to these women had malformed limbs and it was later proved that thalidomide was linked to these birth defects.

thalidomide

The structure of thalidomide contains a tetrahedral carbon atom (coloured red) attached to four different groups. This implies that thalidomide exhibits optical isomerism.

The drug was administered as a racemic mixture; both optical isomers were present in equal proportions. The isomer labelled R prevented morning sickness, whereas the isomer labelled S caused birth defects. Despite the bad reputation of thalidomide, it has since proved useful in alleviating a variety of disorders such as rheumatoid arthritis, leprosy, AIDS, tuberculosis and the rejection of transplanted organs.

The two enantiomers of thalidomide.

SYNTHESIS 1: BOND FISSION, ELECTROPHILES AND NUCLEOPHILES

BOND FISSION

In any reaction in chemistry, bonds in the reactants are broken and bonds in the products are made. The process of breaking bonds is known as **bond fission** and there are two types of bond fission: **homolytic fission** and **heterolytic fission**.

Homolytic fission

Consider the hypothetical molecule **A–B**. When it undergoes **homolytic fission**, one electron of the σ covalent bond ends up on atom **A** and the other electron ends up on atom **B**:

A–B → A· + B·

This bond-breaking process is known as **homolytic** fission because two species of the **same** charge (neutral) are formed. Such fission normally occurs when non-polar covalent bonds are broken. You will notice that each fragment produced has an unpaired electron and can therefore be described as a free radical.

In CfE Higher Chemistry, you came across free radicals when we considered the mechanism of the substitution reaction between methane and chlorine in the presence of ultraviolet light. You will recall that the **initiation step** in the mechanism is the homolytic fission of chlorine molecules to generate chlorine free radicals.

> **DON'T FORGET**
>
> Homolytic bond fission generates free radicals.

Initiation step

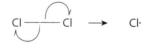

Here, we have used **single-headed curly arrows** or fishhook arrows to indicate the movement of **single** electrons. The tail of the curly arrow shows the source of the electron and the head shows its destination. Using single-headed curly arrows, the mechanism for the methane/chlorine chain reaction is completed below.

Propagation steps

Termination steps

Free radicals are highly reactive species and react with the CH_3Cl and CH_3CH_3 products to produce more free radicals, which, in turn, form even more products. And so it goes on until you end up with a reaction mixture containing lots of different compounds. Each of these compounds will be produced in low yields and will be difficult to isolate. It is for these reasons that reactions involving homolytic fission are unsuitable in the synthesis of organic compounds.

Heterolytic fission

Heterolytic fission normally occurs when polar covalent bonds are broken. Consider the hypothetical molecule A–B again. When it undergoes heterolytic fission, the more electronegative atom of the bond, say B, retains both bonding electrons and ends up as a negatively charged ion. The other atom, A, ends up as a positively charged ion. Using curly arrow notation, we can represent heterolytic fission as shown on the left.

> **DON'T FORGET**
>
> A single-headed curly arrow or fishhook arrow indicates the movement of a single electron.

contd

Notice here that we use a **double-headed curly arrow** because it indicates the movement of a **pair of electrons**. The tail shows the source of the electron pair and the head indicates the destination.

Suppose the $\ddot{B}^\ominus$ ion goes on to react with a $C^\oplus$ ion to form B–C.

You will notice that the head of the curly arrow points midway between the two ions, indicating where the covalent bond forms.

You will gain more experience of using double-headed curly arrows later.

Reactions that proceed via heterolytic fission tend to produce far fewer products than those involving homolytic fission and, as a result, are far better suited in the synthesis of organic compounds.

ELECTROPHILES AND NUCLEOPHILES

We have just seen that when a negatively charged ion reacts with a positively charged ion a covalent bond is formed. The negatively charged ion acts as an electron pair donor, whereas the positively charged ion acts as an electron pair acceptor. The charges on the reactants may be full-blown charges, as shown below, or partial charges ($\delta+$ or $\delta-$). Organic chemists use the terms **nucleophile** and **electrophile** to describe electron pair donors and electron pair acceptors, respectively.

Nucleophiles are negatively charged ions or neutral molecules that are electron-rich. Examples include Br^-, OH^- and NH_3. They have a pair of electrons readily available to donate to an electron

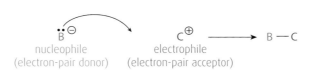

nucleophile · · · · · · electrophile
(electron-pair donor) · · (electron-pair acceptor) · · · B—C

pair acceptor to form a covalent bond. The electron pairs on a nucleophile can be non-bonded electron pairs or bonded electron pairs, such as the π bond in an alkene. Nucleophilic means 'nucleus-loving' and so nucleophiles will be attracted to and will attack species with a positive or partial positive charge.

Electrophiles are positively charged ions or neutral molecules that are deficient in electrons. Examples include H^+, NO_2^+ and SO_3. They are capable of accepting a pair of electrons from an electron pair donor to form a covalent bond. Electrophilic means 'electron-loving' and so electrophiles will be attracted to and will attack species with a negative or partial negative charge.

 ## THINGS TO DO AND THINK ABOUT

1   Using curly arrow notation, write an equation for (a) the homolytic fission of bromine and (b) the heterolytic fission of hydrogen chloride.

2   **a**   The ammonia molecule has four electron pairs surrounding the central nitrogen atom. Which type of electron pair allows ammonia to act as a nucleophile?

     b   Classify each of the following species as a nucleophile or an electrophile:

SYNTHESIS 2: HALOALKANES

Halothane

NAMING HALOALKANES AND STRUCTURAL TYPES

Haloalkanes can be regarded as substituted alkanes in which one or more of the hydrogen atoms is replaced by a halogen atom. They are named in a similar fashion to branched-chain alkanes with the halogen atoms treated like branches. For example, the anaesthetic halothane has the structure shown in the diagram and is called 2-bromo-2-chloro-1,1,1-trifluoroethane.

Like alcohols, there are three structural types of monohaloalkanes: **primary**, **secondary** and **tertiary**. They are classified according to the number of alkyl groups attached to the carbon atom bearing the halogen atom.

(X represents a halogen atom and R, R' and R'' represent alkyl groups.)

primary   secondary   tertiary

The primary monohaloalkanes have one alkyl group attached to the halogen-bearing carbon atom, the secondary monohaloalkanes have two alkyl groups and the tertiary monohaloalkanes have three alkyl groups. Despite the fact that halomethanes, like chloromethane (CH_3Cl), have no alkyl group attached to the halogen-bearing carbon atom, they are still classified as primary monohaloalkanes.

NUCLEOPHILIC SUBSTITUTION REACTIONS OF MONOHALOALKANES

Monohaloalkanes have a polar carbon–halogen bond because the halogen atom has a greater electronegativity than the carbon atom. The slight positive charge on the carbon atom makes monohaloalkanes act as electrophiles and they are therefore susceptible to attack by **nucleophiles**. The nucleophile donates an electron pair to the monohaloalkane and, in so doing, forms a covalent bond with the carbon atom of the C–X bond. At the same time, the halogen atom is thrown out as a halide ion and is replaced or **substituted** by the nucleophile.

Monohaloalkanes undergo **nucleophilic substitution** reactions with:

- **aqueous alkalis to form alcohols**

1-chloropropane   propan-1-ol

For example, when 1-chloropropane is heated under reflux with aqueous sodium or potassium hydroxide, the **alcohol** propan-1-ol is formed.

The OH^- ion is the nucleophile.

Water itself could be used as the nucleophile in this reaction.

- **alcoholic alkoxides to form ethers**

bromoethane   methoxide ion   methoxyethane

For example, when bromoethane is heated under reflux with the alkoxide potassium methoxide in methanol, the **ether**, methoxyethane is formed.

contd

Here, the methoxide ion, CH_3O^-, is the nucleophile. Alkoxides are formed when an alkali metal, such as sodium or potassium, is added to an alcohol. For example, when potassium is added to methanol, potassium methoxide is formed:

$$K + CH_3OH \rightarrow \tfrac{1}{2}H_2 + CH_3O^-K^+$$

You will revisit **ethers** on p. 61.

- **ethanolic potassium (or sodium) cyanide to form nitriles**

For example, when chloromethane is heated under reflux with a solution of potassium (or sodium) cyanide in ethanol, the **nitrile**, ethanenitrile, is formed:

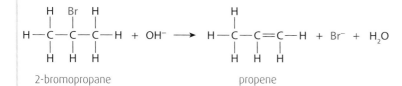

chloromethane   cyanide ion   ethanenitrile

In this case, the cyanide ion, ^-CN, is the nucleophile. Note that the nitrile is called ethanenitrile and not methanenitrile – in naming nitriles the prefix must reflect the number of carbon atoms in the compound, including that in the $-CN$ group.

You will have noticed that the nitrile formed in this reaction contains one more carbon atom than the original monohaloalkane. This makes the reaction very useful in synthetic organic chemistry because it is a way to increase the chain length of an organic compound.

The nitrile produced in the above reaction can be converted into the corresponding carboxylic acid by acid hydrolysis, i.e. reaction with water catalysed by hydrogen ions from the acid.

ethanenitrile   ethanoic acid

DON'T FORGET

Monohaloalkanes react with alkalis to form alcohols, with alcoholic alkoxides to form ethers and with ethanolic cyanides to form nitriles.

VIDEO LINK

For a basic discussion of nucleophilic reactions, watch the video at www.brightredbooks.net

ELIMINATION REACTIONS OF MONOHALOALKANES

Monohaloalkanes can undergo **elimination reactions** when they are heated under reflux with ethanolic potassium (or sodium) hydroxide, i.e. a solution of potassium (or sodium) hydroxide in ethanol. For example, when 2-bromopropane is heated with ethanolic potassium hydroxide, the alkene propene is formed:

2-bromopropane   propene

In the formation of the carbon-to-carbon double bond, the Br atom, together with an H atom on an adjacent carbon atom, has been removed or **eliminated** from the haloalkane and not replaced. This reaction is often referred to as a **base-induced elimination reaction** (see p. 62).

The elimination of hydrogen halides from some monohaloalkanes can result in the formation of two alkenes. Consider 2-bromopentane, for example. You can see from its structure that the elimination of HBr will produce both pent-1-ene and pent-2-ene.

2-bromopentane

DON'T FORGET

In the elimination of a hydrogen halide from a monohaloalkane, the base, potassium (or sodium) hydroxide, must be dissolved in ethanol **not** water.

THINGS TO DO AND THINK ABOUT

Draw structural formulae for the organic products formed when 2-chloro-2-methylbutane is heated under reflux with (a) aqueous potassium hydroxide and (b) ethanolic potassium hydroxide.

ONLINE TEST

Take the test on Synthesis 2 at www.brightredbooks.net

SYNTHESIS 3: MECHANISMS OF NUCLEOPHILIC SUBSTITUTION REACTIONS

A monohaloalkane will undergo nucleophilic substitution by one of two different mechanisms: either an S_N1 mechanism or an S_N2 mechanism.

DON'T FORGET

S_N1 means Substitution, Nucleophilic, **one** species in rate-determining step.

S_N1 MECHANISM

To illustrate the **S_N1 mechanism**, consider the reaction between the tertiary haloalkane 2-bromo-2-methylpropane and the nucleophilic hydroxide ion. A study of the kinetics of the reaction reveals that it has the following rate equation: **rate = $k[(CH_3)_3CBr]$**.

This means that it is first order with respect to the haloalkane and zero order with respect to the hydroxide ions. This implies that the rate-determining step (the slow step) of the mechanism **only** involves the haloalkane. Hence S_N1 means that the reaction involves Substitution by a Nucleophile and that it follows **first**-order kinetics, i.e. only **one** species is involved in the rate-determining step.

The S_N1 mechanism is a two-step process.

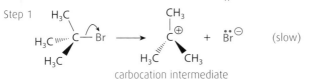

Step 1

carbocation intermediate

Step 2

(slow)

(fast)

Step 1. This is the slow rate-determining step and shows that the 2-bromo-2-methylpropane molecule undergoes **heterolytic fission** of the C–Br bond to form a so-called **carbocation intermediate**.

We use a double-headed curly arrow here to indicate the movement of a pair of electrons. Notice too that the bonds around the positively charged carbon atom in the carbocation intermediate lie in a plane perpendicular to the plane of the paper.

Step 2. This is the fast step and it involves nucleophilic attack on the carbocation by the hydroxide ion.

Although we have shown the hydroxide ion attacking the carbocation from the left-hand side, it could equally well have attacked from the right-hand side (see below). This is a consequence of the carbocation having a planar arrangement of bonds around the central carbon atom.

(fast)

DON'T FORGET

The S_N1 mechanism is a two-step process and proceeds via a carbocation intermediate.

VIDEO LINK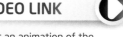

For an animation of the S_N1 mechanism, visit www.brightredbooks.net

S_N2 MECHANISM

To illustrate the **S_N2 mechanism**, consider the reaction between the primary haloalkane bromoethane and the nucleophilic hydroxide ion. A study of the kinetics of the reaction reveals that it has the following rate equation: **rate = $k[CH_3CH_2Br][OH^-]$**.

Hence S_N2 means that the reaction involves Substitution by a Nucleophile and that it follows **second**-order kinetics, i.e. **two** species are involved in the rate-determining step. The S_N2 mechanism involves only one continuous step.

The nucleophilic hydroxide ion attacks the $C^{\delta+}$ atom in the bromoethane from the side opposite to the C–Br bond and begins to form a covalent bond with it. At the same time, the C–Br bond begins to break. A **transition state** is then reached in which the new O–C bond is partially formed and the C–Br bond is partially broken. The reaction is completed by the formation of the full O–C bond and the complete break-up of the C–Br bond.

contd

You will notice that the transition state adopts a trigonal bipyramidal structure with the two C–H bonds and the C–C bond in a plane and the partial bonds lying perpendicular to this plane. The transition state is sometimes referred to as a five-centred transition state because it has five bonds around the central carbon atom.

The mechanism shows that the haloalkane has been pushed inside out, just like an umbrella being blown inside out when it is caught in the wind.

S$_N$1 OR S$_N$2?

When a haloalkane undergoes nucleophilic substitution, how can we tell whether it will proceed via an S$_N$1 mechanism or an S$_N$2 mechanism?

One important factor that helps us to decide is the structure of the haloalkane, i.e. whether it is primary, secondary or tertiary.

In the S$_N$1 mechanism, a carbocation intermediate is formed and this could be a primary, secondary or tertiary carbocation.

Alkyl groups are said to have a positive **inductive effect**. This means they are electron-donating and can push electrons onto the positively charged carbon atom, thus stabilising the carbocation. It follows that tertiary carbocations, with their three alkyl groups, are the most stable species and that primary carbocations, with just one alkyl group, are the least stable species. This suggests that tertiary haloalkanes are most likely to react with a nucleophile via an S$_N$1 mechanism.

The size of the alkyl groups in the haloalkane is important. This is known as a **steric effect**. You will recall that, in the S$_N$2 mechanism, the nucleophile attacks the carbon atom of the C–X bond from the side opposite to the halogen atom. In the case of a tertiary haloalkane, attack from that side is likely to be sterically hindered because three bulky alkyl groups will limit access to the C$^{\delta+}$ atom. Hence tertiary haloalkanes are unlikely to react with nucleophiles via an S$_N$2 mechanism. Primary haloalkanes, on the other hand, have no more than one alkyl group attached to the halogen-bearing carbon atom and so access to the C$^{\delta+}$ atom will be much easier. This suggests that primary haloalkanes are most likely to react with nucleophiles via an S$_N$2 mechanism.

So, by considering the inductive and steric effects, we can suggest which mechanism, S$_N$1 or S$_N$2, is more likely to be favoured by a particular haloalkane.

THINGS TO DO AND THINK ABOUT

Suggest why the compound drawn on the right is unlikely to react with aqueous sodium hydroxide via an S$_N$2 mechanism.

DON'T FORGET

S$_N$2 means Substitution, Nucleophilic, **two** species in the rate-determining step.

DON'T FORGET

The S$_N$2 mechanism is a one-step process and proceeds via a five-centred transition state.

VIDEO LINK

For an animation of the S$_N$2 mechanism, visit www.brightredbooks.net

ONLINE TEST

Be sure to take the test on Synthesis 3 at www.brightredbooks.net

SYNTHESIS 4: ALCOHOLS AND ETHERS

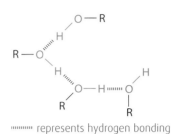

.... represents hydrogen bonding

ALCOHOLS

Physical properties of alcohols

Alcohols have significantly **higher boiling points** than many other organic compounds with similar numbers of electrons per molecule and with similar shapes. The reason is the presence of the **polar −OH group** in the alcohol molecule, which allows **hydrogen bonds** to be set up between the molecules, as shown in the diagram. As hydrogen bonds are stronger than London dispersion forces and permanent dipole–permanent dipole interactions, extra energy is needed to break them, accounting for the higher boiling points of alcohols.

There is a gradation in the **solubility** of alcohols in water. The lower alcohols (methanol, ethanol and propan-1-ol) are miscible with water because they can hydrogen bond with water molecules. Heptan-1-ol and longer chain alcohols are insoluble in water. So, as the chain length increases, the solubility decreases because the long non-polar hydrocarbon part of the molecule masks the polar hydroxyl group.

Preparation of alcohols

Alcohols can be prepared from:

- **monohaloalkanes** by heating under reflux with aqueous sodium or potassium hydroxide (see p. 56).

$$H_3C-CH-CH_3 \longrightarrow H_3C-CH-CH_3$$
$$\hspace{1cm} | \hspace{2cm} + \ OH^- \hspace{2cm} | \hspace{1cm} + \ Br^-$$
$$\hspace{1cm} Br \hspace{4.5cm} OH$$
2-bromopropane · · · · · · · propan-2-ol

  This is a **nucleophilic substitution** reaction.

- **alkenes** by reaction with water in the presence of sulfuric acid as catalyst (see p. 63).

$$H-OH$$
$$H_2C=CH_2 \longrightarrow H_2C-CH_2$$
ethene · · · · · · · · ethanol

  This is an **acid-catalysed addition** or **hydration** reaction.

- **aldehydes and ketones** by reaction with **lithium aluminium hydride** (LiAlH$_4$) dissolved in ether (ethoxyethane). For example:

  R—C—H $\xrightarrow{\text{reduction}}$ R—C—H   R—C—R' $\xrightarrow{\text{reduction}}$ R—C—R'

  aldehyde — primary alcohol   ketone — secondary alcohol

  These are **reduction** reactions. Notice that the aldehyde is reduced to a primary alcohol and the ketone is reduced to a secondary alcohol.

Reactions of alcohols

Alcohols react with:

- **reactive metals**, such as sodium and potassium, to form alkoxides (see p. 57). For example, sodium reacts with ethanol to form sodium ethoxide.

$$Na + CH_3CH_2OH \rightarrow \tfrac{1}{2}H_2 + CH_3CH_2O^-Na^+$$

  This is a **displacement** or **redox** reaction.

- **aluminium oxide** or **concentrated sulfuric acid** or **concentrated phosphoric acid (orthophosphoric acid)** to form **alkenes** (see p. 62).

  H$_3$C—C—C—H $\longrightarrow$ H$_3$C—C=C—H   + H$_2$O

  propan-1-ol — propene

  This is a **dehydration** or **elimination** reaction.

contd

DON'T FORGET

Alcohols can be made from monohaloalkanes, alkenes, aldehydes and ketones.

- **carboxylic acids** or **acid chlorides** to form **esters**.

These are **condensation** or **esterification reactions**. The reaction with the carboxylic acid is slow and requires a catalyst of concentrated sulfuric acid. The reaction with the acid chloride is much faster and an acid catalyst is not required.

$$H_3C - CH_2 - OH \ + \ HO - \overset{\overset{O}{\|}}{C} - CH_3 \ \longrightarrow \ H_3C - CH_2 - O - \overset{\overset{O}{\|}}{C} - CH_3 \ + \ H_2O$$

ethanol ethanoic acid ethyl ethanoate

$$H_3C - CH_2 - OH \ + \ Cl - \overset{\overset{O}{\|}}{C} - CH_3 \ \longrightarrow \ H_3C - CH_2 - O - \overset{\overset{O}{\|}}{C} - CH_3 \ + \ HCl$$

ethanol ethanoyl chloride (an acid chloride) ethyl ethanoate

ETHERS

Naming ethers

Ethers have the general structure **R–O–R'** where **R** and **R'** are alkyl groups that can be either the same or different. An ether can be regarded as an alkane with an alkoxy group attached and is named as such. Alkoxy groups are named by removing the 'yl' from the name of the alkyl substituent and adding 'oxy'. So CH_3O- is named methoxy and CH_3CH_2O- is named ethoxy. To name the ether, the longest carbon chain is identified to give the parent name. This is then prefixed by the name of the alkoxy substituent.

Consider, for example, the ether with the structure drawn on the upper right. The longest chain contains three carbon atoms and so the parent name is propane. An ethoxy group is attached to the second carbon atom, so this ether is called 2-ethoxypropane. The number '2' is needed to distinguish this ether from ethoxypropane.

2-ethoxypropane

ethoxypropane

Physical properties of ethers

Ethers have much lower boiling points than their isomeric alcohols because hydrogen bonding does not occur between ether molecules. The reason for this is that the highly electronegative oxygen atom is not directly bonded to a hydrogen atom. Ether molecules, however, can form hydrogen bonds with water molecules. This explains why ethers with a low molecular mass, such as methoxymethane and methoxyethane, are soluble in water. Larger ethers are insoluble in water, which makes them useful for extracting organic compounds from aqueous reaction mixtures.

Ethers are volatile and highly flammable. They are used as solvents because they are relatively inert chemically and most organic compounds dissolve in them. Being volatile, these solvents are easily removed by distillation.

Preparation of ethers

Ethers can be prepared by refluxing a haloalkane with an alkoxide (see p. 56). For example, ethoxyethane is made by heating chloroethane with a solution of potassium ethoxide in ethanol.

chloroethane ethoxyethane

The reaction taking place is **nucleophilic substitution**.

DON'T FORGET

Ether molecules cannot form hydrogen bonds with other ether molecules, but they can form hydrogen bonds with water molecules.

ONLINE TEST

To take a test on Synthesis 4, visit www.brightredbooks.net

 THINGS TO DO AND THINK ABOUT

In recent years, there has been a lot of interest in cyclic ethers like the one shown here.

Known as crown ethers because of their crown-like shape, these ethers contain cavities that are ideal for forming complexes with metal ions. It is this property that allows ordinary salts to dissolve in organic solvents. For example, potassium permanganate is usually insoluble in benzene, but readily dissolves in benzene if [18]-crown-6 ether is added. This solution is useful because it allows oxidation with potassium permanganate to be carried out in organic solvents. The potassium ion (shown in green) is just the right size to fit into the cavity in the crown ether.

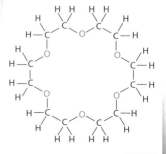

SYNTHESIS 5: ALKENES

PREPARATION OF ALKENES

Alkenes can be prepared by

- **dehydration of alcohols** (see p. 60)

The vapour of the alcohol can be passed over hot **aluminium oxide**, or the alcohol can be treated with **concentrated sulfuric acid** or **concentrated phosphoric acid** (orthophosphoric acid).

During dehydration, the $-OH$ group is removed, along with an H atom on an adjacent carbon atom. In this case, two alkenes are formed, although but-2-ene is the major product. With some alcohols, such as butan-1-ol and propan-2-ol, only one alkene is formed.

You will recall that this reaction can also be described as an **elimination reaction**, i.e. a reaction in which the elements of a simple molecule, such as water, are removed from the organic molecule and not replaced. Concentrated phosphoric acid is preferred to concentrated sulfuric acid when dehydrating alcohols because more side reactions occur with the latter and it tends to lead to charring.

- **base-induced elimination of hydrogen halides from monohaloalkanes** (see p. 57)

This reaction is achieved by heating the monohaloalkane under reflux with ethanolic potassium (or sodium) hydroxide, i.e. potassium (or sodium) hydroxide dissolved in ethanol. The reaction is referred to as a **base-induced elimination reaction** and to demonstrate more clearly the role of the base in the reaction, it is worth considering the mechanism involved. This is illustrated for the reaction between 2-bromopropane and ethanolic potassium hydroxide:

The basic OH^- ion initially attacks an H atom on the carbon atom adjacent to the halogen-bearing carbon atom in the haloalkane. It forms a bond with this H atom and an HO–H molecule is generated. At the same time, the pair of electrons in the C–H bond moves between the two carbon atoms on the left-hand side of the haloalkane to form a double bond. Finally, the C–Br breaks heterolytically, releasing a Br^- ion. You are not required to know this mechanism, but it helps to explain why the elimination reaction is referred to as base-induced.

Like the dehydration of some alcohols, the elimination of hydrogen halides from monohaloalkanes can result in the formation of two alkenes. For example, heating 2-chlorobutane with ethanolic potassium hydroxide produces but-1-ene and but-2-ene.

REACTIONS OF ALKENES

Alkenes undergo **addition reactions** with **hydrogen** to form **alkanes**, with **halogens** to form **dihaloalkanes**, with **hydrogen halides** to form **monohaloalkanes** and with **water** to form **alcohols**. For example:

contd

DON'T FORGET

An elimination reaction is one in which the elements of a small molecule, such as water or a hydrogen halide, are removed from an organic molecule and not replaced.

The addition reaction of an **alkene** with:

- **hydrogen** is also known as **hydrogenation** and is catalysed by nickel or platinum
- a **halogen** is also known as **halogenation**
- a **hydrogen halide** is also known as **hydrohalogenation**
- **water** is also known as **hydration** and is catalysed by acids

MARKOVNIKOV'S RULE

We have just seen that when H–H or Br–Br or H–Br or H–OH is added to but-2-ene, only one product is formed. However, when a **hydrogen halide** or **water** is added to an unsymmetrical alkene, i.e. one in which the groups attached to one carbon of the double bond are not identical to the groups attached to the other carbon atom, two products are formed. For example, when hydrogen chloride is added to the unsymmetrical alkene but-1-ene, both 2-chlorobutane and 1-chlorobutane are formed:

2-Chlorobutane is the major product of this reaction, but how can this be predicted? It was the Russian chemist, Vladimir Markovnikov, who formulated a rule to answer this question.

Markovnikov's rule states that when H–X or H–OH is added to an unsymmetrical alkene, the major product is the one in which the H atom ends up attached to the carbon atom of the double bond that already has the greater number of hydrogen atoms bonded to it. If you look at the structure of but-1-ene, you can see that the carbon atom (coloured green) on the right of the double bond has more H atoms attached to it than the carbon atom on the left (coloured red). So, on adding hydrogen chloride, the H atom of the HCl molecule will attach itself to the right-hand carbon atom of the double bond, giving 2-chlorobutane as the major product. Markovnikov's rule is empirical and it was only when the mechanisms of these addition reactions were worked out that they could be explained (see pp. 64–65).

 DON'T FORGET

Markovnikov's rule states that the main product of the reaction between an unsymmetrical alkene and a hydrogen halide or water is the one in which the hydrogen atom adds to the carbon atom of the double bond that already has the greater number of hydrogen atoms attached to it.

VIDEO LINK

For an animation of the application of Markovnikov's rule, visit www.brightredbooks.net

 ONLINE TEST

Test yourself on your knowledge of Synthesis 5 at www.brightredbooks.net

 THINGS TO DO AND THINK ABOUT

1 1-Methylcyclohexene reacts with hydrogen chloride to form two products. Draw a structural formula for each of the two products and name the major product.

SYNTHESIS 6: MECHANISMS OF ELECTROPHILIC ADDITION REACTIONS

HALOGENATION

The mechanism for the halogen–alkene addition reaction is a two-step process and is illustrated below using bromine and ethene.

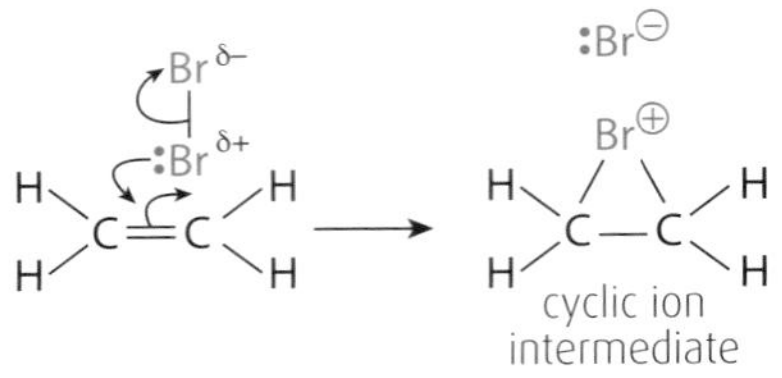

Step 1

As the bromine molecule approaches the double bond in ethene, it becomes polarised. The electron-rich double bond in ethene 'pushes' the electrons in the bromine molecule towards the Br atom that is remote from the double bond. This Br atom gains a slight negative charge, leaving the other Br atom with a slight positive charge. The $Br^{\delta+}$ of the bromine molecule attacks the ethene and a **cyclic ion intermediate** is formed along with a Br^- ion. The movement of electron pairs in the process is indicated in the diagram using double-headed curly arrows.

In this first step, the **bromine molecule** is acting as an **electrophile** and the **ethene** is acting as a **nucleophile**.

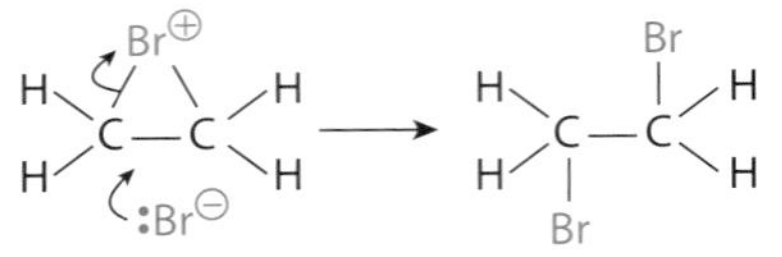

Step 2

The Br^- ion then attacks the cyclic ion intermediate from the side opposite to where the Br atom is attached. This happens because the Br atom in the intermediate is large and so prevents access to that side of the cyclic ion intermediate.

In the second step, the Br^- **ion** is acting as a **nucleophile** while the **cyclic ion intermediate** is acting as an **electrophile**.

DON'T FORGET

The mechanism for the electrophilic addition of a halogen to an alkene proceeds via a cyclic ion intermediate.

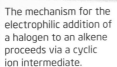

HYDROHALOGENATION

The mechanism for the hydrogen halide–alkene addition reaction is again a two-step process and is illustrated below using hydrogen bromide and propene.

Step 1

The H–Br molecule is the electrophile and is already polarised. Its $H^{\delta+}$ atom attacks the double bond in propene, forming an intermediate **carbocation**. At the same time, the bond in the H–Br molecule breaks heterolytically and a Br^- ion is generated.

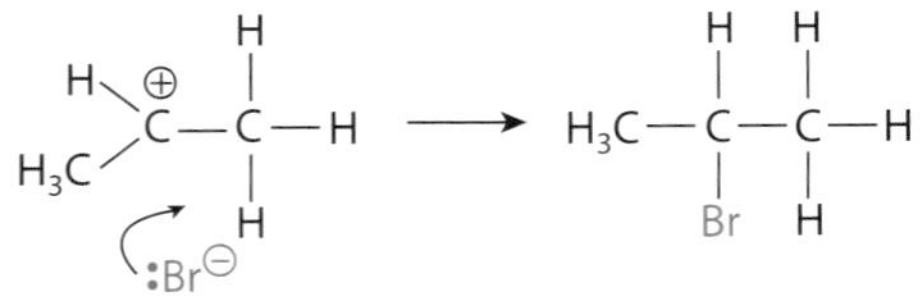

Step 2

The second step involves nucleophilic attack of the Br^- ion on the carbocation. In this mechanism, unlike in the halogenation reaction, the Br^- ion can attack from either side of the carbocation.

You will remember that, when a hydrogen halide reacts with an unsymmetrical alkene, such as propene, two products are formed: 2-bromopropane and 1-bromopropane.

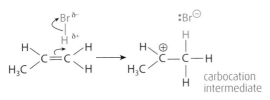

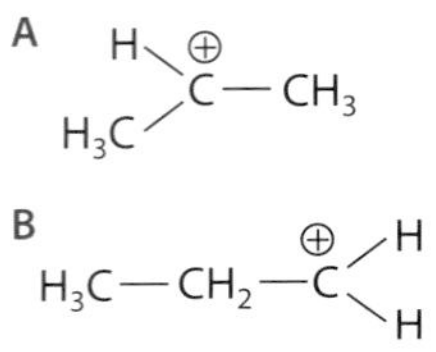

The carbocations that are formed to generate these two products are shown on the left. You will recall that alkyl groups can exert a positive inductive effect (see p. 59), i.e. they can 'push' electrons towards the positively charged carbon atom in the carbocation and so stabilise it. Therefore carbocation A will be more stable than carbocation B because it has two alkyl groups directly attached to the positively charged carbon atom, whereas there is only one alkyl group in carbocation B.

contd

Consequently, 2-bromopropane, rather than 1-bromopropane, will be the major product of the reaction. This helps to explain why Markovnikov's rule applies to the addition of a hydrogen halide to an unsymmetrical alkene.

ACID-CATALYSED HYDRATION

The mechanism for the acid-catalysed hydration reaction is very similar to that for the hydrohalogenation of alkenes and also proceeds via a carbocation intermediate. It is outlined below using water and propene.

Step 1

The hydrogen ion of the acid catalyst is an electrophile and attacks the electron-rich double bond in the propene molecule to form a carbocation.

carbocation intermediate

Step 2

The carbocation then undergoes rapid nucleophilic attack by a water molecule to give a protonated alcohol molecule (an alcohol with a hydrogen ion attached).

Step 3

The protonated propan-2-ol is a strong acid and readily loses a proton (hydrogen ion) to give the final product, propan-2-ol. You will notice that the hydrogen ion used up in the first step is regenerated in the final step, thus confirming its role as a catalyst.

protonated alcohol

Like the hydrohalogenation reaction, the hydration of unsymmetrical alkenes, such as propene, leads to two products. As well as propan-2-ol, propan-1-ol is also formed. In accordance with Marovnikov's rule, propan-2-ol is the major product. Again, this is due to the greater stability of carbocation A compared with carbocation B.

VIDEO LINK

For a comprehensive overview of the electrophilic addition of a hydrogen halide to an unsymmetrical alkene and the role of Markovnikov's rule, visit www.brightredbooks.net

DON'T FORGET

The mechanism for the electrophilic addition of a hydrogen halide or water to an alkene proceeds via a carbocation intermediate.

ONLINE TEST

For an online test on Synthesis 6, visit www.brightredbooks.net

 THINGS TO DO AND THINK ABOUT

In the early days of alkene chemistry, some researchers found that the hydrohalogenation of alkenes followed Markovnikov's rule, while others found that the same reaction did not. For example, when freshly distilled but-1-ene was exposed to hydrogen bromide, the major product was 2-bromopropane, as expected by Markovnikov's rule. However, when the same reaction was carried out with a sample of but-1-ene that had been exposed to air, the major product was 1-bromopropane formed by anti-Markovnikov addition. This caused considerable confusion, but the mystery was solved by the American chemist, Morris Kharasch, in the 1930s. He realised that the samples of alkenes that had been stored in the presence of air had formed peroxide radicals. The hydrohalogenation thus proceeded by a radical chain reaction mechanism and not via the mechanism involving carbocation intermediates as when pure alkenes were used.

SYNTHESIS 7: CARBOXYLIC ACIDS AND AMINES

CARBOXYLIC ACIDS

Preparation of carboxylic acids

Carboxylic acids can be prepared by

- **oxidising primary alcohols or aldehydes**

The **primary alcohol** or **aldehyde** is heated under reflux with **acidified potassium dichromate solution**. For example:

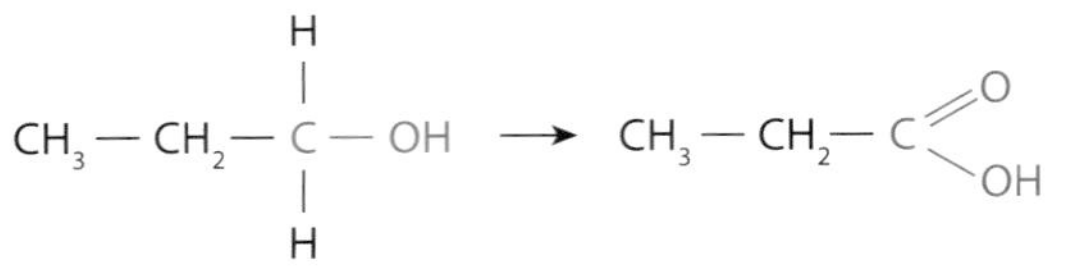

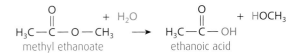

propan-1-ol → propanoic acid

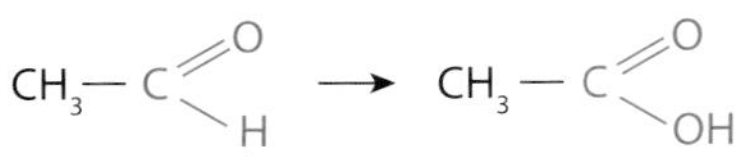

ethanal → ethanoic acid

Although the primary alcohol is initially oxidised to an aldehyde, it is difficult to stop the reaction at that stage because further oxidation takes place to give the carboxylic acid.

$$CH_3-CH_2-CH_2-CN \xrightarrow{H_2O/H^+} CH_3-CH_2-CH_2-COOH$$

butanenitrile → butanoic acid

- **hydrolysing nitriles**

The **nitrile** is heated under reflux with an **aqueous acid** and undergoes **hydrolysis**.

The hydrogen ions of the acid catalyse the reaction.

- **hydrolysing esters**

$$H_3C-\overset{O}{\overset{\|}{C}}-O-CH_3 + H_2O \longrightarrow H_3C-\overset{O}{\overset{\|}{C}}-OH + HOCH_3$$

methyl ethanoate → ethanoic acid

The **ester** is heated under reflux with an **aqueous acid** or an **aqueous alkali** as catalyst and undergoes **hydrolysis**.

When an alkali, say sodium hydroxide, is used as a catalyst, this helps to drive the equilibrium position to the side of the products. The reason is that the sodium hydroxide reacts with the ethanoic acid to form sodium ethanoate. Ethanoic acid, however, is easily generated from the sodium ethanoate by adding a strong acid such as hydrochloric acid.

- **hydrolysing amides**

The **amide** is heated under reflux with an **aqueous acid** or an **aqueous alkali** as catalyst and undergoes **hydrolysis**.

$$H_3C-CH_2-\overset{O}{\overset{\|}{C}}-\overset{H}{\overset{|}{N}}-CH_3 + H_2O \rightleftharpoons H_3C-CH_2-\overset{O}{\overset{\|}{C}}-OH + H_2N-CH_3$$

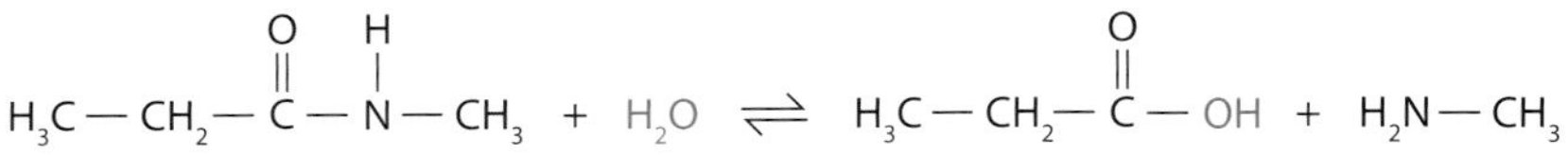

an amide → propanoic acid

As in the hydrolysis of esters, using an alkali as catalyst 'pushes' the equilibrium position to the right.

Reactions of carboxylic acids

In aqueous solution, **carboxylic acids** behave as typical acids and form **salts** on reaction with:

- some **metals**. For example: $Mg + 2CH_3CH_2COOH \rightarrow H_2 + Mg^{2+}(CH_3CH_2COO^-)_2$
- **carbonates**. For example: $Na_2CO_3 + 2CH_3COOH \rightarrow CO_2 + H_2O + 2Na^+CH_3COO^-$
- **alkalis**. For example: $KOH + HCOOH \rightarrow H_2O + K^+HCOO^-$

Carboxylic acids also react with:

- **alcohols** to form **esters**.

DON'T FORGET

Carboxylic acids can be prepared by oxidising primary alcohols and aldehydes and hydrolysing nitriles, esters and amides.

contd

This reaction is a **condensation reaction** and is **catalysed** by **concentrated sulfuric acid** or **concentrated phosphoric acid**.

$$CH_3-CH_2-CH_2-OH + HO-\overset{\overset{O}{\|}}{C}-CH_3 \rightleftharpoons CH_3-CH_2-CH_2-O-\overset{\overset{O}{\|}}{C}-CH_3 + H_2O$$

propan-1-ol   ethanoic acid   propyl ethanoate

- **amines** to form alkylammonium salts, which on heating form **amides**.

$$H_3C-NH_2 + HO-\overset{\overset{O}{\|}}{C}-CH_3 \rightarrow H_3C-NH_3^{+-}O-\overset{\overset{O}{\|}}{C}-CH_3 \xrightarrow{heat} H_3C-\overset{\overset{H}{|}}{N}-\overset{\overset{O}{\|}}{C}-CH_3 + H_2O$$

methylamine   ethanoic acid   methylammonium ethanoate   an amide

- **lithium aluminium hydride (LiAlH$_4$)** in ether (ethoxyethane) to form **primary alcohols**. For example:

$$H_3C-CH_3-\overset{\overset{O}{\|}}{C}-OH \rightarrow H_3C-CH_3-CH_2-OH$$

propanoic acid   propan-1-ol

This is a **reduction reaction** and the LiAlH$_4$ is such a strong reducing agent that it reduces the carboxylic acid directly to the primary alcohol.

VIDEO LINK

For a basic coverage of carboxylic acids, visit www.brightredbooks.net

AMINES

Structural types of amines and nomenclature

Amines are **organic derivatives** of **ammonia** in which one or more hydrogen atoms in ammonia has been replaced by alkyl groups. There are three structural types of amine: primary, secondary and tertiary. They are classified according to the number of alkyl groups attached to the nitrogen atom.

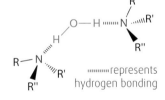

primary   secondary   tertiary
(R, R' and R" represent alkyl groups)

The most common method of **naming amines** is to prefix the word 'amine' with the names of the alkyl groups (arranged in alphabetical order) attached to the nitrogen atom. For example, $CH_3CH_2NHCH_3$ is called ethylmethylamine and $(CH_3)_3N$ is called trimethylamine.

Physical and chemical properties of amines

Primary and secondary amines contain a polar N–H bond and so have **hydrogen bonds** between their molecules. No such bonds can be set up between the molecules of tertiary amines because they do not contain a hydrogen atom directly bonded to the highly electronegative nitrogen atom. This is why primary and secondary amines have higher boiling points than their isomeric tertiary amines.

····· represents hydrogen bonding

Amines with a low molecular mass are soluble in water because they can form hydrogen bonds with water molecules. This is true even for tertiary amines, as can be seen in the diagram.

Amines, like ammonia, are **weak bases** (see p. 31) and dissociate to a slight extent in aqueous solution. In the reaction, the non-bonded pair (lone pair) of electrons on the nitrogen atom in the amine molecule accepts a proton (hydrogen ion) from the water molecule, thus generating alkylammonium ions and hydroxide ions. The latter ions make the solution alkaline. For example: $CH_3NH_2(aq) + H_2O(l) \rightleftharpoons CH_3NH_3^+(aq) + OH^-(aq)$

Amines react with

- **mineral acids**, such as hydrochloric, sulfuric and nitric acids, to form **salts**. For example:

$CH_3CH_2NH_2(aq) + HNO_3(aq) \rightarrow CH_3CH_2NH_3^+NO_3^-(aq)$ (ethylammonium nitrate)

- **carboxylic acids** to form **salts**. On heating these salts, water is lost and amides are formed as shown above.

DON'T FORGET

Primary, secondary and tertiary amines can form hydrogen bonds with water molecules, but only primary and secondary amines have hydrogen bonds between their molecules.

ONLINE TEST

Test yourself on the content in Synthesis 7 at www.brightredbooks.net

THINGS TO DO AND THINK ABOUT

Which of the following isomeric amines has the lowest boiling point?

A $C_4H_9NH_2$ **B** $C_3H_7NHCH_3$ **C** $C_2H_5NHC_2H_5$ **D** $C_2H_5N(CH_3)_2$

SYNTHESIS 8: AROMATIC HYDROCARBONS

STRUCTURE AND BONDING IN BENZENE

Aromatic hydrocarbons (or arenes) are a subset of the larger set of hydrocarbons and the simplest of these is **benzene**. It is a colourless liquid and has a molecular formula of C_6H_6. The molecular formula shows that benzene is deficient in hydrogen atoms and suggests that it is an unsaturated hydrocarbon.

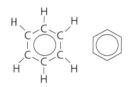

Kekule structures of benzene.

Kekule, a German chemist, was the first to propose a structure for benzene in 1865. It was a cyclic structure of alternating single and double bonds. The Kekule structure, however, does not fit all the evidence that chemists have since collected. For example, when benzene is added to a bromine solution, rapid decolourisation does **not** take place. This implies that **benzene resists addition reactions** and is much more stable than a typical unsaturated hydrocarbon. The reason for this becomes clear when we examine more closely the structure and bonding in benzene.

Structural formulae of benzene.

Benzene is now more commonly represented by the structural formula shown on the left. The molecule is flat and has a regular hexagonal shape. The six carbon-to-carbon bonds in the ring are equal in length and equal in strength and are intermediate between a carbon-to-carbon single bond and a carbon-to-carbon double bond.

In the benzene molecule, each carbon atom is **sp^2 hybridised** and the three half-filled **sp^2** hybrid orbitals form σ **bonds** with a hydrogen atom and two neighbouring carbon atoms. This leaves an electron occupying a p orbital on each carbon atom. Each of these p orbitals overlaps side-on with p orbitals on neighbouring carbon atoms, and a π **electron cloud** is formed, as shown in the diagram.

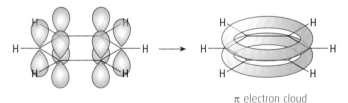

π electron cloud

The benzene molecule therefore contains **12 σ bonds** (shown in black) and **a π electron cloud** (shown in pink). The six electrons that occupy the π electron cloud are not tied to any one carbon atom, but are shared by all six carbons. They are **delocalised** and represented by a ring in the structural formulae.

It is important to note that the Kekule structure for benzene and related compounds has not been abandoned – it is still widely used.

DON'T FORGET

Bonding in benzene can be described in terms of sp^2 hybridisation, σ bonds and a π electron cloud containing delocalised electrons.

VIDEO LINK

For an overview of the structure and bonding in benzene, visit www.brightredbooks.net

REACTIONS OF BENZENE

Benzene is unusually stable and it is the delocalised electrons that account for this stability. The presence of the delocalised electrons also explains why benzene does not undergo addition reactions. Addition reactions would disrupt the electron delocalisation and so reduce the stability of the ring. Substitution reactions, on the other hand, can occur without any such disruption and the stability of the benzene ring is maintained. The delocalised electrons in the π electron cloud make benzene susceptible to attack by electrophiles (electron pair acceptors). As a result, benzene undergoes **electrophilic substitution reactions** and some of these are outlined at the top of the next page. Note that the electrophiles are shown in red, the reagents in blue and the reaction names in green.

contd

methylbenzene

akylation
CH_3^+
$CH_3Cl/AlCl_3$

chlorination
Cl^+
$Cl_2/FeCl_3$

chlorobenzene

concentrated H_2SO_4

$HOSO_2^+$
sulfonation

NO_2^+
nitration

concentrated HNO_3 and H_2SO_4 acids

benzenesulfonic acid

nitrobenzene

As well as **chlorination**, benzene can undergo **bromination** when bromine is used as the reagent along with aluminium chloride or iron(III) chloride as catalyst. The electrophiles, Cl^+ and Br^+, are generated by the reaction between the halogen and the catalyst:

$$Cl_2 + AlCl_3 \text{ or } FeCl_3 \rightarrow Cl^+ + [AlCl_4]^- \text{ or } [FeCl_4]^-$$

$$Br_2 + AlCl_3 \text{ or } FeCl_3 \rightarrow Br^+ + [AlCl_3Br]^- \text{ or } [FeCl_3Br]^-$$

The electrophile in the **nitration** of benzene is the **nitronium** ion, NO_2^+, which is generated by the reaction between concentrated nitric and sulfuric acids:

$$HNO_3 + 2H_2SO_4 \rightarrow NO_2^+ + 2HSO_4^- + H_3O^+$$

In the **sulfonation** of benzene, the electrophile, $HOSO_2^+$, is generated from the concentrated sulfuric acid:

$$H_2SO_4 + H_2SO_4 \rightarrow HOSO_2^+ + HSO_4^- + H_2O$$

Oleum, which is concentrated sulfuric acid with sulfur trioxide added, can also be used as the reagent in sulfonation and the electrophile is SO_3.

When benzene is alkylated, it reacts with a **haloalkane** in the presence of aluminium chloride as a catalyst. In the example shown, chloromethane is used and the electrophile CH_3^+ is generated from its reaction with aluminium chloride:

$$CH_3Cl + AlCl_3 \rightarrow CH_3^+ + [AlCl_4]^-$$

 DON'T FORGET

Benzene resists addition reactions, but undergoes electrophilic substitution reactions.

OTHER AROMATIC HYDROCARBONS

There are many other aromatic hydrocarbons, i.e. compounds like benzene, which contain rings of six carbon atoms stabilised by electron delocalisation. For example, if one of the hydrogen atoms in benzene is replaced by a methyl group, then a hydrocarbon called **methylbenzene** (or toluene) is formed. It has the structural formulae shown. Methylbenzene can be regarded as a substituted alkane. One of the hydrogen atoms in methane has been substituted by a $-C_6H_5$ or  group, which is known as a **phenyl group**. So an alternative name for methylbenzene is **phenylmethane**. Other examples of aromatic hydrocarbons include naphthalene and anthracene.

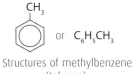
Structures of methylbenzene (toluene).

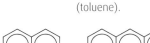

naphthalene

anthracene

Like benzene, other aromatic hydrocarbons will undergo electrophilic substitution reactions.

 THINGS TO DO AND THINK ABOUT

Both benzene and graphite contain delocalised electrons. Why does graphite conduct electricity, yet benzene does not?

ONLINE TEST

Take the test on Synthesis 8 at www.brightredbooks.net

SYNTHESIS 9: SYNTHETIC ORGANIC CHEMISTRY

INTRODUCTION

Synthesis, or the making of molecules, is a fundamental part of organic chemistry. Millions of organic compounds have now been synthesised from simpler materials. These substances include many that also occur in nature, such as **vitamin C**, as well as entirely new compounds. Some, such as **cubane**, are largely of theoretical interest and give chemists the opportunity to study special kinds of bonding and reactivity. Others, such as the artificial sweetener **saccharin** and the drug **aspirin** have become a part of everyday life.

vitamin C   cubane   saccharin   aspirin

ORGANIC REACTIONS

A knowledge of **organic reactions** is vital in devising ways of synthesising new molecules or so-called target molecules. So far, in your study of organic chemistry, you have encountered the following organic reactions.

- **Substitution,** in which an atom or group of atoms in a molecule is replaced by another atom or group of atoms. This reaction is commonly used in preparing alcohols, ethers and nitriles from monohaloalkanes.
- **Addition,** where atoms or groups of atoms bond to two atoms, initially joined by a multiple bond in the reactant molecule. These are the most common reactions undergone by alkenes.
- **Elimination,** where the elements of a small molecule are removed from the reactant molecule and not replaced. Examples include making alkenes from alcohols or monohaloalkanes.
- **Condensation,** in which two molecules combine to form a larger molecule and a small molecule, such as H_2O or HCl, is eliminated. Such reactions take place when esters are formed from alcohols and carboxylic acids (or acid chlorides).
- **Hydrolysis,** where a molecule reacts with water and breaks down into smaller molecules. For example, amides can be hydrolysed to carboxylic acids and amines.
- **Oxidation** is when there has been an increase in the O : H ratio on going from reactant to product. Examples include the conversion of a primary alcohol to a carboxylic acid via an aldehyde and the conversion of a secondary alcohol to a ketone.
- **Reduction** is when there has been a decrease in the O : H ratio on going from reactant to product. For example, carboxylic acids can be reduced directly to a primary alcohol.

Given equations, you must be able to identify these types of reaction. You must also be able to use them when devising a synthetic route.

DON'T FORGET

Given an equation for an organic reaction, you must be able to identify the reaction type and you must be able to use these reactions in designing synthetic routes.

FUNCTIONAL GROUP INTERCONVERSIONS

The **functional group** of an organic molecule is its reactive part and, as such, is responsible for the reactions that molecule will undergo. We have now accumulated a fair bit of knowledge about different functional groups and the connections between them. These **functional group interconversions** are summarised in the diagram on p. 71.

contd

It is important to be able to look at a molecular structure and deduce the possible reactions it can undergo. Take an **alkene**, for example. It has a π **bond** that makes it electron-rich and able to attack **electrophiles** such as water, halogens and hydrogen halides in **electrophilic addition** reactions. **Haloalkanes**, on the other hand, contain polar carbon–halogen bonds because the halogen is more electronegative than carbon. This makes them susceptible to attack by **nucleophiles**, such as hydroxide, cyanide and alkoxide ions, in **nucleophilic substitution** reactions.

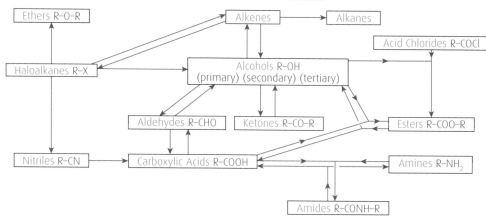

Functional group interconversions.

DEVISING SYNTHETIC ROUTES

With your knowledge of organic reactions, functional groups and functional group interconversions, you are now in a position to apply this knowledge in devising a synthetic route from a given reactant to a final product.

Consider the conversion of chloroethane (CH_3CH_2Cl) to propan-1-ol ($CH_3CH_2CH_2OH$).

You know that the C–Cl bond in chloroethane is polar, with the C atom having a δ+ charge. This implies that chloroethane is an electrophile and will react with nucleophiles. Another key point to note is that the chain length has been increased by one carbon atom. You know this can be achieved by introducing a cyano group (−CN), i.e. making a nitrile.

The first step would be to heat the chloroethane with ethanolic potassium cyanide to form propanenitrile. This is a **nucleophilic substitution** reaction with the CN⁻ ion acting as the nucleophile.

You will recall that nitriles are easily converted into carboxylic acids by hydrolysis. This involves heating the nitrile with an aqueous acid. The hydrogen ions of the acid catalyse the reaction.

The final step is to convert the carboxylic acid into a primary alcohol by heating it with lithium aluminium hydride ($LiAlH_4$) dissolved in ether (ethoxyethane). This is a **reduction** reaction and delivers the target molecule, propan-1-ol.

It is normal practice to write an equation for each step, to give the reagents and conditions used, and to state the type of reaction taking place.

DON'T FORGET

You must be able to devise a synthetic route, with no more than three steps, from a given reactant to a final product.

VIDEO LINK

An alternative strategy in devising a synthetic route to a target molecule is known as **retrosynthesis**. To find out more about this, visit www.brightredbooks.net

ONLINE TEST

Test your knowledge of Synthesis 9 at www.brightredbooks.net

THINGS TO DO AND THINK ABOUT

Describe how you would carry out the following conversions:

a $CH_3COCH_3 \rightarrow CH_3CH(Cl)CH_2Cl$

b $CH_3CH_2CHO \rightarrow CH_3CH_2COOCH_2CH_2CH_3$

EXPERIMENTAL DETERMINATION OF STRUCTURE 1

A number of experimental techniques are carried out in organic chemistry to confirm that the correct compound has been synthesised during a reaction, or to identify unknown compounds. Some of these techniques are laboratory-based and are discussed in the Researching Chemistry section. Organic chemists rely heavily on a number of other techniques to identify compounds. These include elemental microanalysis, mass spectrometry, infrared spectrometry and ^{1}H NMR spectrometry.

DON'T FORGET

The empirical formula shows the simplest whole number ratio of the different atoms in a compound.

DON'T FORGET

Elemental microanalysis is used to determine the masses of the elements present in a sample of an organic compound to work out its empirical formula.

ELEMENTAL MICROANALYSIS

Elemental microanalysis (or **combustion analysis**) can be used to determine the **empirical formula** of an organic compound.

In modern combustion analysers, a tiny sample (about 2 mg) is accurately weighed and oxidised at a high temperature in an oxygen atmosphere. The product mixture of CO_2, H_2O, N_2 and SO_2 is separated by gas chromatography and the mass of each component is measured using a thermal conductivity detector. From these product masses, the mass of each of the elements C, H, N and S in the sample can be derived. If oxygen is present in the sample, its mass can be determined by subtracting the total mass of the other elements present from the mass of the original sample. The empirical formula can be calculated from the element masses using the following method.

C, H, N, S
in sample

$\downarrow O_2$

$CO_2(g) + H_2O(g) + N_2(g) + SO_2(g)$

Calculating the empirical formula

Suppose the complete combustion of 1·75 mg of an organic compound produced 3·51 mg of CO_2 and 1·43 mg of H_2O (1 mg = $\frac{1}{1000}$ g). No other product was formed.

1 mol CO_2 (44·0 g) contains 1 mol C (12·0 g)

Mass of C in sample = $3·51 \times 10^{-3} \times 12·0/44·0 = 9·57 \times 10^{-4}$ g

1 mol H_2O (18·0 g) contains 2 mol H (2·0 g)

Mass of H in sample = $1·43 \times 10^{-3} \times 2·0/18·0 = 1·59 \times 10^{-4}$ g

It can be seen that the mass of carbon and hydrogen in the sample does not account for the total mass of the sample that was subjected to combustion analysis. As no other product was formed, the original sample must also have contained oxygen. The mass of oxygen in the original sample can be determined as follows:

Mass of O in sample = $1·75 \times 10^{-3} - 9·57 \times 10^{-4} - 1·59 \times 10^{-4} = 6·34 \times 10^{-4}$ g

Element	C	H	O
Mass (g)	$9·57 \times 10^{-4}$	$1·59 \times 10^{-4}$	$6·34 \times 10^{-4}$
Number of moles	$9·57 \times 10^{-4}/12·0$ $= 7·98 \times 10^{-5}$	$1·59 \times 10^{-4}/1·0$ $= 1·59 \times 10^{-4}$	$6·34 \times 10^{-4}/16·0$ $= 3·96 \times 10^{-5}$
Mole ratio	$7·98 \times 10^{-5}/3·96 \times 10^{-5}$ $= 2·02 \ (2)$	$1·59 \times 10^{-4}/3·96 \times 10^{-5}$ $= 4·02 \ (4)$	$3·96 \times 10^{-5}/3·96 \times 10^{-5}$ $= 1·00 \ (1)$

ONLINE TEST

Test your empirical formula calculations at www.brightredbooks.net

Empirical formula = C_2H_4O

MASS SPECTROMETRY

Mass spectrometry is a technique used to determine the accurate molecular mass and structural features of an organic compound.

contd

In mass spectrometry, a minute sample (about 1×10^{-4} g) of the unknown organic compound is vaporised and injected into the mass spectrometer, where it is bombarded by high energy electrons. The energy is sufficient to knock electrons out of the molecules and, as a result, these molecules break into smaller positively charged ion fragments.

These **positively charged ions**, mostly with a +1 charge, are accelerated by a high voltage electric field into a strong magnetic field that deflects them into a series of separate ion paths according to their mass/charge (m/z) ratio. Positive ions with lower mass/charge ratios are deflected more than those with higher ratios. Each separated ion path is detected and a spectrum is recorded.

The mass spectrum shown is that for **ethanol** (CH_3CH_2OH). The peak with the highest m/z ratio provides the gram formula mass of the organic compound. In the example, this appears at m/z = 46 and confirms the gram formula mass of ethanol as 46 g. This peak arises from the so-called **molecular ion** $[CH_3CH_2OH]^+$ (the molecule with one electron removed). The table below the mass spectrum shows the formula of the molecular ion and the formulae of the ion fragments that are responsible for some of the other peaks in the spectrum.

Mass spectrometry is often used alongside elemental microanalysis. The mass spectrum below is of a sample that was analysed previously which was found to have an empirical formula C_2H_4O.

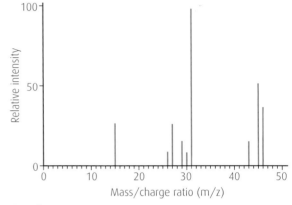

m/z ratio of peak	Ion fragment
15	$[CH_3]^+$
29	$[CH_3CH_2]^+$
31	$[CH_2OH]^+$
45	$[CH_3CH_2O]^+$
46	$[CH_3CH_2OH]^+$

From this spectrum, the gram formula mass of the sample can be determined to be 88 g. The gram formula mass for the empirical formula is 44 g [2(12·0) + 4(1·0) + 1(16·0)]. So the molecular formula for the sample must be $2 \times C_2H_4O = C_4H_8O_2$.

It is worth noting that the label on the y-axis of a mass spectrum can be 'relative intensity' or 'percentage abundance'.

THINGS TO DO AND THINK ABOUT

Sometimes elemental microanalysis results are given as percentages by mass. The process used to calculate the empirical formula from the percentage by mass is similar to that just shown, assuming the total mass of the sample to be 100 g.

For example, a compound **X** has the composition; C 40·00%, H 6·71%, O 53·29%.

a   Determine the empirical formula for compound **X**.

b   The mass spectrum of compound **X** is shown. Determine the molecular formula for compound **X**.

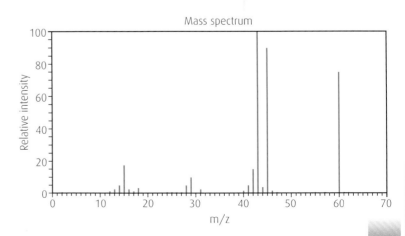

EXPERIMENTAL DETERMINATION OF STRUCTURE 2

INFRARED SPECTROSCOPY

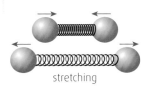

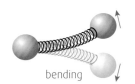

stretching   bending

A useful model of a bond, in which the bond is represented as a spring joining two atoms. There are a number of different types of bond vibration; this diagram shows the stretching and bending modes.

Infrared radiation comprises that part of the electromagnetic spectrum that lies between microwaves and visible light (see p. 6). When it is absorbed by organic compounds, the energy is sufficient to cause the **bonds** within the molecules to **vibrate,** but not enough to break the bonds.

The wavelength of the infrared radiation that is absorbed when a bond vibrates depends on the type of atoms that make up the bond and the stiffness (strength) of the bond. In general, light atoms joined by stiff bonds absorb radiation of a shorter wavelength (higher energy) than heavier atoms joined by looser bonds. **Infrared spectroscopy** makes use of these characteristics and is an important analytical tool; it can be used to identify certain **bonds** and **functional groups** in organic molecules.

An infrared spectrum can be obtained for a sample of an organic compound regardless of its physical state (solid, liquid, gas or dissolved in a solvent). Infrared radiation is passed through the sample in the spectrometer. Some wavelengths are absorbed, causing bond vibrations within the molecules. The transmitted radiation then passes to a detector where the intensity at different wavelengths is measured. An infrared spectrum, like that shown in the diagram, is obtained.

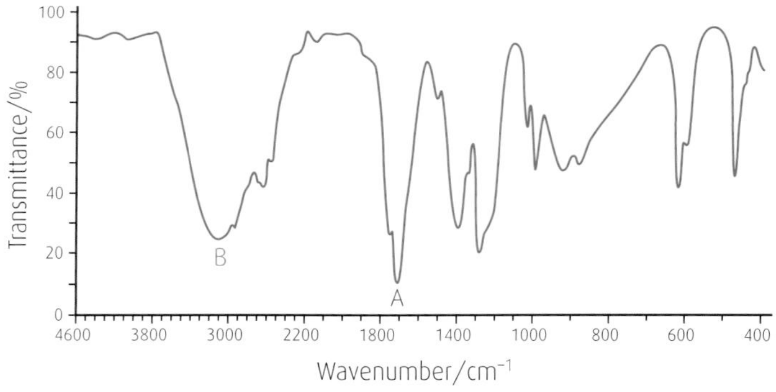

DON'T FORGET

The absorption of infrared radiation causes bonds within a molecule to vibrate and infrared spectroscopy can be used to identify functional groups in an organic molecule.

Infrared spectrum of ethanoic acid.

VIDEO LINK

Watch a video clip about infrared spectroscopy at www.brightredbooks.net

ONLINE TEST

Head to www. brightredbooks.net and test yourself on the experimental determination of structure.

In an infrared spectrum, an absorption corresponds to a 'peak' pointing towards the bottom of the graph. The absorption is expressed in terms of wavenumber. The wavenumber is the reciprocal of wavelength, i.e. wavenumber = $\dfrac{1}{\text{wavelength}} = \dfrac{1}{\lambda}$ and the units are normally cm^{-1}.

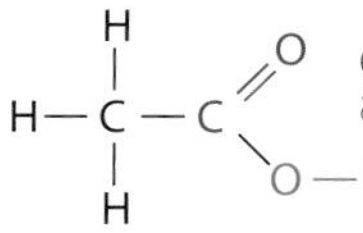

ethanoic acid

Absorption peak A, at 1700 cm^{-1}, is due to stretching of the C=O bond. The broad peak B, at 2600–3400 cm^{-1}, corresponds to stretching of the hydrogen-bonded O–H bond in the acid.

contd

As particular types of vibration always occur at a similar wavenumber, it is possible to build up a table of characteristic absorptions. Such a table is given on p. 14 of the SQA Data Booklet. If you examine this table, you will see, for example, that an absorption in the wavenumber range 2260–2215 cm^{-1} is indicative of a nitrile group and is due to stretching of the C≡N bond. So, given the infrared spectrum of an unknown organic compound and a table of characteristic absorptions, it should be possible to identify the functional groups present in the compound. In most cases, however, more information is required to determine the full structure.

THINGS TO DO AND THINK ABOUT

The infrared spectrum of a compound is shown below.

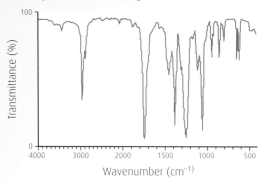

The molecular formula of the compound is $C_4H_8O_2$. Using information from the infrared spectrum and p. 14 in the SQA Data Booklet, suggest a structural formula for the compound.

EXPERIMENTAL DETERMINATION OF STRUCTURE 3

PROTON NUCLEAR MAGNETIC RESONANCE SPECTROSCOPY (^{1}H NMR)

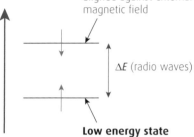

High energy state
This hydrogen nucleus aligned against external magnetic field

ΔE (radio waves)

Low energy state
This hydrogen nucleus aligned with external magnetic field

External magnetic field

Some atomic nuclei can spin about their own axes. For example, the ^{1}H nucleus (a hydrogen nucleus or proton) can spin in one of two directions: clockwise and anticlockwise. As a result, protons behave as tiny magnets and, when placed between the poles of a powerful magnet, some align themselves with the field of the magnet while others align against it. Those protons aligned with the field have a slightly lower energy than those aligned against it.

The energy difference between the two states corresponds to the radio frequency region of the electromagnetic spectrum. So, when protons are exposed to radio waves, energy is absorbed to promote those in the lower energy state to the higher energy state. In effect, the protons 'flip' from being aligned with the magnetic field to being aligned against it. As the protons fall back to the lower energy state, the same radio frequency that was absorbed is emitted. This can be measured with a radio receiver. This phenomenon is known as **proton nuclear magnetic resonance (^{1}H NMR)**.

Low resolution ^{1}H NMR spectroscopy

^{1}H NMR spectroscopy is a powerful analytical tool and gives information about:

- how many different chemical environments the protons in an organic molecule can exist in
- how many protons are in each of these environments
- the type of proton environment

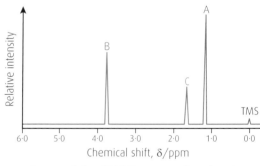

Low resolution ^{1}H NMR spectrum for ethanol.

Take ethanol, for example. You can see from its structural formula that the protons are in three different chemical environments: the H nuclei in the CH_3 group, the H nuclei in the CH_2 group and the H nucleus in the OH group.

$$H-\overset{\displaystyle H}{\underset{\displaystyle H}{C}}-\overset{\displaystyle H}{\underset{\displaystyle H}{C}}-O-H \quad \text{ethanol}$$

The three peaks A, B and C in the spectrum correspond to the three different chemical environments of the protons. The area under each peak is proportional to the number of protons in that environment. In this case, the areas under peaks A, B and C are in the ratio **3:2:1** corresponding to the **three** protons in the CH_3 group, the **two** protons in the CH_2 group and the **one** proton in the OH group.

Notice the small peak labelled **TMS**. TMS is short for tetramethylsilane, $Si(CH_3)_4$, which is used as a standard against which all absorptions due to other proton environments are measured. TMS is assigned a value of zero and the difference between the protons in TMS and the protons in other chemical environments is known as the **chemical shift**, which is given the symbol δ. The chemical shift is measured in parts per million (ppm). Chemical shift values for protons in different chemical environments are given on p. 16 of the SQA Data Booklet.

If you examine this chart, you will see that:

- protons in a CH_3 group have a chemical shift in the range 0·9–1·5 ppm and so peak A is due to the CH_3 protons in ethanol
- protons in a CH_2 group in an alcohol have a chemical shift in the range 3·5–3·9 ppm and so peak B is due to the CH_2 protons in ethanol
- protons in an OH group in an alcohol have a chemical shift in the range 1·0–5·0 ppm and so peak C must be due to the OH proton in ethanol.

DON'T FORGET

An ^{1}H NMR spectrum provides information about how many different chemical environments of hydrogen nuclei (protons) there are in an organic molecule and the relative numbers of protons in each of these environments. The chemical shift gives information about the types of environments these protons are in.

contd

High resolution ¹H NMR spectroscopy

High resolution ¹H NMR spectra are obtained by using a radio frequency higher than that used for low resolution spectra (typically around 300–500 MHz compared with 90–200 MHz). This results in more detailed spectra being produced.

The low and high resolution spectra for methyl propanoate are shown on the right.

The low resolution ¹H NMR spectrum for methyl propanoate has three peaks, showing that there are three proton environments – these are circled on the structural formula. The high resolution ¹H NMR spectrum shows each of these peaks in more detail and we can see that they are made up of multiples of peaks, known as **multiplets**.

For there to be more than one peak in a given proton environment there must be hydrogen atoms within that environment that are experiencing slightly different magnetic fields. These very slight differences in chemical shift are due to the influence of the hydrogen atoms on the neighbouring carbon atom (these hydrogen atoms have a magnetic field of their own and can be aligned with or against the external magnetic field).

The additional detail provided by a high resolution spectrum allows more information to be determined about the structure of the compound. Analysing the multiplets allows the neighbouring proton environment to be identified. This can be done using the **n + 1 rule**, where n is the number of hydrogen atoms attached to the next-door carbon atom and $n + 1$ is the number of peaks that will be seen in the cluster.

The table shows the different multiplet patterns you may encounter.

Name of multiplet	Number of peaks in spectrum, $n + 1$	Number of hydrogen atoms on the next-door carbon, n
Doublet	2	1
Triplet	3	2
Quartet	4	3

Let us now apply this rule to analyse the high resolution spectrum for ethyl ethanoate.

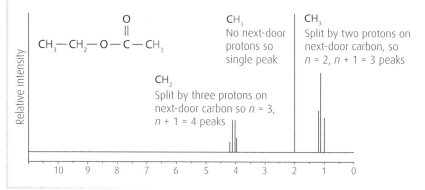

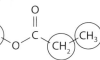

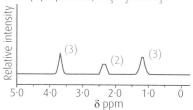

Low resolution nmr spectrum for methyl propanoate, $CH_3CH_2COOCH_3$

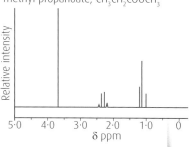

High resolution nmr spectrum for methyl propanoate, $CH_3CH_2COOCH_3$

VIDEO LINK

For a video clip about ¹H NMR spectroscopy, head to www.brightredbooks.net

ONLINE

For more information about ¹H NMR spectroscopy, follow the link at www.brightredbooks.net

ONLINE TEST

Test your knowledge of high resolution ¹H NMR spectroscopy at www.brightredbooks.net

THINGS TO DO AND THINK ABOUT

As hydrogen is the most common element in the human body, it is not surprising that nuclear magnetic resonance has found applications in the field of medicine as **magnetic resonance imaging** or **MRI**.

NMR imaging in medicine is based on the time it takes for hydrogen nuclei (protons) in the unstable high energy state to 'relax' or return to the low energy state. These relaxation times are different for protons in fat, muscle (proteins), blood and bone because of differences in their chemical environments. The relaxation times are enhanced by computer, to produce a magnetic resonance image. A major advantage of MRI scanning over X-rays is that the patient is exposed to radio frequency radiation, avoiding the damage caused by higher energy X-rays.

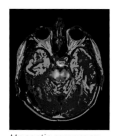

Magnetic resonance imaging scan.

PHARMACEUTICAL CHEMISTRY

ONLINE

Head to www.brightredbooks.net to see a time line for drug development.

DON'T FORGET

Medicines are those drugs that have a beneficial effect on the body.

VIDEO LINK

Watch the short video clip showing how modern medicines are made at www.brightredbooks.net

INTRODUCTION

The pharmaceutical industry in the UK contributes enormously to the economy. In Scotland alone, business related to the pharmaceutical industry contributed £380 million to the gross value of the economy in 2008.

A medicine takes, on average, more than 12 years to develop to the stage when it will be licensed for use. This process costs around £1·15 billion. Most compounds that are tested will never make it to licence – some may have unacceptable side effects, others may not work any better than existing treatments.

There is a misconception that drugs and medicines are quite different. The term 'drug' carries with it the connotation of addiction, abuse and crime, but, in fact, medicines are just a subset of drugs. **Drugs** are defined as substances that can alter the biochemical processes in the body and **medicines** are those drugs that have a beneficial effect. Most drugs work by binding to receptors. Receptors are often protein molecules that are present on the surface of cells or enzymes (catalytic receptors) that catalyse chemical reactions.

As well as containing the drug needed to cause the beneficial effect, sometimes referred to as the active ingredient, medicines often have other ingredients added. For example, a 'filler' substance may be added to bulk out the medicine if the amount of active ingredient is very small. Some medicines are sweetened and some are coated to allow them to be swallowed easily.

DRUG DEVELOPMENT

Since ancient times, the curative powers of brews or potions derived from certain plants have been recognised. Examples include:

- the bark of the willow tree used to relieve pain, lower fever and to reduce inflammation
- opium used as a sedative and painkiller
- the bark of the cinchona tree used to treat malaria

As chemical knowledge and understanding improved, chemists were able to determine the structures of some of these pharmacologically active compounds. This led to the synthesis of the active compounds themselves and to the synthesis of their derivatives. As a result, the range of effective medicines rapidly expanded.

Take aspirin, for example. It has its origins in salicin, the active ingredient in willow bark. When salicin is hydrolysed it produces glucose and salicyl alcohol; the latter can be oxidised to salicylic acid. Salicylic acid was also used as a medicine, but it caused irritation and bleeding in the stomach and intestines. However, when salicylic acid is treated with ethanoic anhydride, acetylsalicylic acid (**aspirin**) is produced.

Nowadays, computers play an important part in the design and development of medicines. For example, molecular modelling software allows chemists to study how potential medicines will interact with receptors in the body and to determine how their structures can be modified to enhance their effect.

Medicinal chemists aim to make compounds that will be effective in treating disease and have minimal side effects.

salicin

H₂O

salicyl alcohol + glucose

oxidation

salicylic acid

acetylsalicylic acid (aspirin)

Aspirin has proved to be a very effective medicine with few side effects, unlike salicylic acid, which causes stomach irritation.

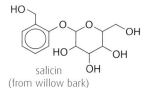

salicin (from willow bark)

morphine (from opium)

quinine (from cinchona bark)

Skeletal structures of some of the pharmacologically active compounds found in plant materials.

CLASSIFICATION OF MEDICINES

Most medicines can be classified as **agonists** or **antagonists** according to the response they trigger when bound to a receptor site. An **agonist** mimics the body's naturally active molecule and, on binding to the receptor site, it triggers the same response as the natural molecule. An **antagonist**, on the other hand, binds more strongly to the receptor site and prevents the naturally active molecule from binding. As a result, the antagonist molecule blocks the site and so the natural response is not triggered.

An example of an **agonist medicine** is salbutamol, which is used in the treatment of asthma. Asthma attacks are caused when the airways in the lungs narrow and become blocked with mucus. The body responds to this by releasing adrenaline, which binds to receptors and triggers the dilation of the airways. The medicine salbutamol binds more strongly to the receptor sites than adrenaline and triggers a dilation of the airways. In doing so, it triggers a response similar to the body's naturally active compound.

An example of an **antagonist** medicine is propranolol, which is used to treat high blood pressure. It too acts by binding to adrenaline receptor sites, but it does not trigger a response. The propranolol therefore blocks the receptor sites and prevents the action of the body's natural compound.

DON'T FORGET

An agonist medicine triggers a response like the body's naturally active compound, while an antagonist medicine produces no response by preventing the action of the body's naturally active compound.

ONLINE

Try designing active drug molecules at www.brightredbooks.net

DESIGNING MEDICINES

To design more effective medicines, chemists need to consider the structure of compounds that are active for a particular receptor or active site and to determine the important functional groups present in these compounds. These functional groups allow the compound to interact with the active site. These interactions can be any van der Waals' forces (hydrogen, permanent dipole–permanent dipole interactions, London dispersion forces) and even ionic bonds. Equally important is the distance between these functional groups. If too few, or too many, carbon atoms are present between the important groups on the molecule, then these groups will not be able to interact with the correct part of the active site of the protein. This is referred to as the structural fragment of a medicine that confers its pharmacological activity.

Active sulfonamides	Inactive sulfonamides

The table shows the structural formulae of some sulfonamides. Some sulfonamides are antibacterial agents (shown in green in the first column of the table) and some (in the second column, in red) have no antibacterial activity. By examining both sets of structures you can see that the structural fragment that makes sulfonamide active is:

This structural fragment may bind to an active site through hydrogen bonds and London dispersion forces as follows:

ONLINE TEST

Head to www.brightredbooks.net and test yourself on this topic.

can form hydrogen bonds with active site

Some possible interactions between a sulfonamide structural fragment and an active site.

hydrogen bond can be made if the active site has an O–H or N–H bond

may form London dispersion forces with active site

THINGS TO DO AND THINK ABOUT

1 Draw the structural formula of acetylsalicylic acid shown on p. 78 and highlight the types of interactions that may be formed between it and a protein receptor.

GRAVIMETRIC ANALYSIS

STOICHIOMETRY AND QUANTITATIVE ANALYSIS

A balanced chemical equation is a stoichiometric equation. It tells us the numbers of moles of reactants and products in a chemical reaction. A quantitative reaction is one in which the substances react completely according to the mole ratios given by the balanced equation.

A chemist will often need to know the exact quantity of a substance present in a given sample of a chemical. This can be determined by carrying out a quantitative reaction and using the stoichiometry of the reaction to determine the amount of substance.

Two methods commonly used in quantitative analysis are gravimetric and volumetric analyses.

CALCULATIONS BASED ON VOLUMETRIC AND GRAVIMETRIC ANALYSES

In most calculations associated with volumetric and gravimetric analyses, it is sensible to change the reacting quantities into moles. For substances in solution the formula used is:

$$n = c \times V$$

where n = number of moles, c = concentration (mol l^{-1}) and V = volume of solution (l).

For solids or pure substances where the mass has been measured, the formula used is:

$$n = \frac{mass}{GFM} \text{ where } n = \text{number or moles,}$$

the mass is measured in grams and the GFM is the gram formula mass of the substance.

DON'T FORGET ➕

These two formulae for calculating the number of moles, n, are very important.

GRAVIMETRIC ANALYSIS

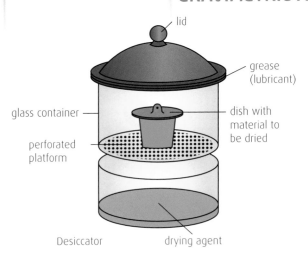

lid

grease (lubricant)

glass container

perforated platform

dish with material to be dried

Desiccator

drying agent

In gravimetric analysis, the mass of an element or compound present in a substance is determined by changing that substance into another substance of known chemical composition and formula, which can then be readily isolated, purified and weighed. The final product must be dried completely. This is done by the process of 'heating to constant mass' – heating the substance, allowing it to cool in a dry atmosphere inside a desiccator, then weighing it. The process is repeated until a constant mass is obtained, showing that all the water has been driven off.

One method of gravimetric analysis involves precipitation reactions. The substance being analysed is reacted with a reagent to form a precipitate. For example, silver(I) ions in solution may be reacted with a reagent containing chloride ions to cause a precipitate of silver(I) chloride to form. The precipitate is then separated from the filtrate and the filtrate is tested to ensure the reaction has gone to completion by addition of more reagent. The precipitate is then washed, dried and then weighed. This is called precipitation conversion.

The accuracy of this method relies on the accuracy of the balance used. The initial and final masses are recorded and the difference between the two values gives the mass of the product.

contd

Another type of gravimetric analysis involves heating a substance to evaporate any volatile products. This is known as volatilisation conversion. As an example, gravimetric analysis can be used to determine the amount of water in hydrated barium chloride.

A known quantity of hydrated barium chloride, $BaCl_2.nH_2O$ was weighed accurately, by difference, in a crucible. The hydrated barium chloride was heated in the crucible using a blue Bunsen flame and then allowed to cool in a desiccator. The crucible and its contents were then reweighed. The cycle of heating, cooling in the desiccator and weighing was repeated until a constant mass had been achieved. At this stage, it was presumed that all the water had been driven off. This process of driving off volatile products (water in this example) is known as a volatilisation conversion.

ONLINE TEST

Test yourself on gravimetric and volumetric calculations at www.brightredbooks.net

Results

Mass of empty crucible = 32·67 g

Mass of crucible + hydrated barium chloride = 35·03 g

Therefore mass of hydrated barium chloride = 35·03 − 32·67 g = 2·36 g

Mass of crucible + anhydrous barium chloride = 34·69 g
(after constant mass had been reached)

Therefore, mass of anhydrous barium chloride = 34·69 − 32·67 = 2·02 g

Mass of water driven off = 2·36 − 2·02 = 0·34 g

Number of moles of $BaCl_2$, $n = \dfrac{\text{mass}}{\text{GFM}} = \dfrac{2·02}{208·3} = 0·00970$ mol

Number of moles of water, $n = \dfrac{\text{mass}}{\text{GFM}} = \dfrac{0·34}{18} = 0·0189$ mol

ONLINE

To remind yourself how to weigh samples accurately, watch the video clip at www.brightredbooks.net

The ratio of the number of moles of $BaCl_2$ to the number of moles of H_2O = 0·00970 : 0·0189 = 1 : 1·95, which is approximately 1 : 2. So the formula of hydrated barium chloride is $BaCl_2.2H_2O$.

THINGS TO DO AND THINK ABOUT

1 Calculate the mass of sodium carbonate needed to make 250 cm³ of a 0·10 mol l⁻¹ standard solution of sodium carbonate.

2 To determine the silver composition of an alloy, a piece of alloy weighing 10·48g was dissolved in nitric acid and the resulting solution was diluted to 1·00 litre in a standard flask. 0·20 moll⁻¹ hydrochloric acid was added to 100·0 cm³ of this solution until precipitation of silver(I) chloride was complete.

   The precipitate was recovered by filtration, washed and dried to constant mass and was found to have a mass of 0·63 g.

   Calculate the percentage by mass of silver in the coin.

VOLUMETRIC ANALYSIS

Volumetric analysis involves using a solution of accurately known concentration, a standard solution, in a quantitative reaction to determine the concentration of the other reactant. The procedure is known as **titration**. One solution is measured quantitatively into a conical flask using a pipette. The other solution is dispensed from a burette until a permanent colour change appears in the solution in the conical flask.

A 'rough' titration is usually carried out, followed by more accurate titrations until concordant results are obtained. Concordant results are within either 0·1 or 0·2 cm³ of each other, depending on the accuracy required. The mean or average value of the concordant results is used in the calculations.

VIDEO LINK

Check out the video clip showing titration at www.brightredbooks.net

DON'T FORGET

You must know the characteristics of a primary standard.

Structure of potassium hydrogenphthalate.

VIDEO LINK

Watch the video clip showing how to make a standard solution from a solid solute at www.brightredbooks.net

Redox titration using potassium permanganate as the oxidising reagent and self-indicator.

STANDARD SOLUTIONS

A **standard solution** is a solution for which an accurate concentration is known. A standard solution can be prepared directly from a **primary standard**. This involves weighing out the primary standard accurately and dissolving it in deionised water in a beaker. The solution, plus all the rinsings, are then transferred into a standard flask and made up to the graduation mark with more deionised water. A primary standard must have the following characteristics: be available in a high state of purity; be stable when solid and when in solution; be soluble in water and have a reasonably high GFM to reduce the percentage errors when weighing.

Examples of primary standards include sodium carbonate (Na_2CO_3), oxalic acid ($H_2C_2O_4.2H_2O$), potassium hydrogen phthalate ($KH(C_8H_4O_4)$), silver nitrate ($AgNO_3$), potassium iodate (KIO_3) and potassium diochromate ($K_2Cr_2O_7$).

Sodium hydroxide is not a primary standard – it has a relatively low GFM and readily absorbs moisture, making it unstable as a solid. The solution also absorbs carbon dioxide and so its concentration is not constant. The accurate concentration of a solution of sodium hydroxide can be determined by titrating it with a solution of a primary standard such as potassium hydrogenphthalate.

The two types of titration that you have encountered so far are **acid–base** and **redox** titrations. During a titration, the experimenter looks for a permanent colour change in the solution in the conical flask, usually due to the presence of an indicator. This is known as the **end-point** of the reaction. The **equivalence point** is the point at which the reaction is *just* complete. The ideal situation is when the equivalence point and the end-point are exactly the same. Choosing the correct indicator and carrying out titrations very carefully and accurately help to ensure that the equivalence point and the end-point are very close (see p. 37).

REDOX TITRATIONS

During a redox titration an oxidising agent reacts with a reducing agent. The reducing agent is an electron donor and is itself oxidised during the reaction. The oxidising agent is an electron acceptor and is reduced during the reaction. A very useful reagent in redox titrations is acidified permanganate (H^+/MnO_4^-), which is an excellent oxidising agent and has the advantage that it also acts as its own indicator.

The purple permanganate solution is usually placed in the burette and the reducing agent (plus some sulfuric acid to provide the H^+ ions) is placed in the conical flask. The purple permanganate ions change to colourless Mn^{2+} ions as they are added to the reducing agent. The end-point is observed when all the reducing agent has been used up and the purple MnO_4^- ions no longer react. The colour of the reaction mixture in the conical flask becomes a permanent light purple or pink colour.

COMPLEXOMETRIC TITRATIONS

Complexometric titrations are based on reactions in which complexes are formed (see p. 22). A common reagent used in complexometric titrations is ethylenediaminetetraacetic acid (EDTA). It is often used to determine the concentration of metal ions present in a solution.

For example, EDTA can be used to determine the percentage of nickel present in a nickel salt by complexometric titration. EDTA is a hexadentate ligand that binds in a 1 : 1 ratio with most metal ions, such as Ni^{2+}, forming a stable octahedral complex as shown in the diagram.

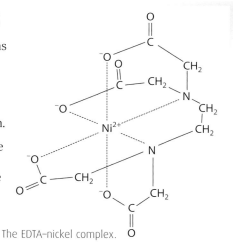

The EDTA–nickel complex.

 ONLINE TEST

Test yourself on volumetric calculations at www.brightredbooks.net

 **DON'T FORGET**

A complex consists of a central metal ion surrounded by ligands. EDTA is commonly used in complexometric titrations to determine the concentration of metal ions in solution because it forms complexes with metals ions in a 1 : 1 ratio.

Example:

In an experiment to determine the percentage of nickel in hydrated nickel(II) sulfate, 2·63 g of the nickel(II) sulfate were weighed accurately, dissolved in water and diluted to 100 cm^3 in a standard flask. A 20·0 cm^3 volume of this solution was pipetted into a conical flask along with an indicator solution. This solution was titrated against a 0·100 mol l^{-1} EDTA solution until the end-point was observed. The titrations were repeated until concordant results were obtained.

Results

Theoretical calculation

GFM of hydrated nickel(II) sulfate, $NiSO_4.6H_2O = 262.8$ g

$\% \ Ni = \dfrac{58.7}{262.8} \times 100 = 22.3\%$

 **DON'T FORGET**

Concordant titration results are within 0·1 or 0·2 cm^3 of one another.

Experimental results

Mass of hydrated nickel(II) sulfate used = 2·63 g

	Rough titre	First titre	Second titre
Initial burette reading (cm^3)	0·1	0·2	20·4
Final burette reading (cm^3)	20·8	20·4	40·5
Volume of EDTA added (cm^3)	20·7	20·2	20·1

Average of concordant results $= \dfrac{20.2 + 20.1}{2} = 20.15 \, cm^3$

Concentration of EDTA solution = 0·10 mol l^{-1}

Number of moles of EDTA used to react with 20 cm^3 of nickel(II) solution:

$V \times c = 0.02015 \times 0.10 = 2.015 \times 10^{-3}$ mol

Therefore the number of moles of Ni^{2+} ions in 20 $cm^3 = 2.015 \times 10^{-3}$ mol

Number of moles of Ni^{2+} ions in the total volume of 100 cm^3
$= 2.015 \times 10^{-3} \times 5 = 1.0075 \times 10^{-2}$ mol

Therefore the mass of nickel in salt $= n \times GFM = 1.0075 \times 10^{-2} \times 58.7 = 0.5914$ g

From these results the % mass of nickel in the salt $= \dfrac{0.5914}{2.63} \times 100 = 22.5\%$

 ## THINGS TO DO AND THINK ABOUT

A 10·0 cm^3 volume of a liquid drain cleaner containing sodium hydroxide was diluted to 250 cm^3 in a standard flask. Samples of this diluted solution with volumes of 25·0 cm^3 were pipetted into a conical flask and titrated against a 0·220 mol l^{-1} sulfuric acid solution. The average of the concordant titres was 17·8 cm^3. Calculate the mass of sodium hydroxide in one litre of the drain cleaner.

MORE ON VOLUMETRIC ANALYSIS

There is one other type of volumetric analysis that we will consider here: back titrations.

BACK TITRATIONS

A back titration – also known as an indirect titration – allows the concentration of an unknown solution to be determined by reacting it with a known excess of a reagent. The quantity of the excess reagent is determined by titration with a second reagent.

This method is used in the determination of the quantity of aspirin present in a sample. As it is insoluble in water, aspirin cannot be determined by direct titration.

A sample of aspirin of accurately known mass is reacted with a known excess amount of sodium hydroxide solution. The alkali first catalyses the hydrolysis of aspirin to ethanoic acid and salicylic acid (2-hydroxybenzoic acid) and then neutralises these acids. The overall balanced equation for the reaction is:

As an excess of sodium hydroxide is used, the amount remaining is determined by titrating it against a standard solution of sulfuric acid. The chemical equation for the reaction taking place during the titration is:

$$2NaOH + H_2SO_4 \rightarrow 2H_2O + Na_2SO_4$$

The difference between the initial number of moles of NaOH and the number of moles of NaOH in excess allows the mass of the aspirin in the tablet to be calculated.

The following results from a back titration experiment can be used to illustrate how this is done.

Example:

A 1·50 g mass of aspirin was hydrolysed with 25·0 cm³ of 1·00 mol l⁻¹ NaOH solution. After the hydrolysis was complete, the reaction mixture was transferred, with rinsings, to a 250 cm³ standard flask and made up to the graduation mark with distilled water. The solution was mixed thoroughly and 25·0 cm³ was pipetted into a conical flask, along with a few drops of phenolphthalein indicator. This was titrated with 0·0500 mol l⁻¹ sulfuric acid solution until the end-point of the titration was indicated by the colour change from pink to colourless. The titrations were repeated until concordant results were obtained.

Results

Titre		Trial experiment	Experiment 1	Experiment 2
Burette reading/cm³	Initial	1·5	17·1	0·6
	Final	17·1	32·3	15·7
Titre volume/cm³		15·6	15·2	15·1

The mean titre volume was therefore 15·15 cm³.

Number of moles of sulfuric acid used in titration = 0·01515 × 0·0500 = 7·575 × 10⁻⁴ mol

1 mole of sulfuric acid reacts with 2 moles of sodium hydroxide

Number of moles of sodium hydroxide left in 25·0 cm³ of the hydrolysed solution
= 2 × 7·575 × 10⁻⁴ = 1·515 × 10⁻³ mol

Number of moles of sodium hydroxide left in 250·0 cm³ of the hydrolysed solution
= 10 × 1·515 × 10⁻³ = 1·515 × 10⁻² mol

ONLINE

For another back titration example, watch the video at www.brightredbooks.net

ONLINE TEST

Test your knowledge of volumetric analysis at www.brightredbooks.net

contd

Number of moles of sodium hydroxide added to aspirin tablets initially
$= 0.0250 \times 1.00 = 2.50 \times 10^{-2}$ mol

Number of moles of sodium hydroxide that reacted with aspirin
$= 2.50 \times 10^{-2} - 1.515 \times 10^{-2} = 9.85 \times 10^{-3}$ mol

2 moles of sodium hydroxide reacts with 1 mole of aspirin

Therefore the number of moles of aspirin in the 1.50 g sample
$= (9.85 \times 10^{-3})/2 = 4.925 \times 10^{-3}$ mol

Mass of aspirin in the 1.50 g sample $= n \times$ GFM $= 4.925 \times 10^{-3} \times 180.0 = \mathbf{0.887}$ g

USE OF A CONTROL IN AN EXPERIMENT

When carrying out such an experiment to determine the mass of aspirin in a sample, a control experiment will often be performed. To do this, we use a sample that contains a known mass of aspirin. This allows the validity of the technique to be checked. For example, a sample of pure aspirin of accurately known mass, say 1.00 g, could be treated in the same manner as the described experiment. If the experimentally determined quantity of aspirin is very close to the known value of 1.00 g, then it can be concluded that this method of determining the aspirin content is valid and therefore any results obtained by this method will be reliable.

 ## THINGS TO DO AND THINK ABOUT

A student carried out an experiment to determine the percentage of calcium carbonate present in eggshells. A 0.456 g mass of eggshell was weighed accurately and then reacted with 25.0 cm³ of 0.500 mol l⁻¹ HCl. This mixture was transferred to a 100 cm³ standard flask, with rinsings, and the solution was made up to the graduation mark with distilled water. Samples of volume 25.0 cm³ were titrated with 0.0500 mol l⁻¹ NaOH and the average titre was found to be 22.5 cm³. Calculate the percentage by mass of $CaCO_3$ in the eggshell.

PRACTICAL SKILLS AND TECHNIQUES 1

The next four pages will look at techniques that can be used together as part of one experiment. To illustrate this, we will consider an experiment to determine the percentage by mass of manganese in a steel paper clip using colorimetry.

PREPARING STANDARD SOLUTIONS

You should already be familiar with preparing standard solutions from a solid solute. To refresh your knowledge, refer to p. 82.

It is often necessary to prepare (accurately) dilute solutions of a standard solution. For the final concentration of the diluted solution to be accurately known, this dilution must be carried out using accurate equipment. Standard solutions used to prepare a calibration graph are often prepared in this way.

The initial standard solution is called the **stock solution**.

In an experiment to determine the percentage by mass of manganese in a steel paper clip, it is necessary to prepare various concentrations of standard potassium permanganate solutions. You will learn more about this experiment on p. 88. A standard $0\cdot0010$ mol l^{-1} solution of potassium permanganate is often used as a stock solution in this experiment. Dilutions of the stock solution are prepared by accurately transferring a known volume of the stock solution, using a pipette or a burette, into a volumetric flask (standard flask). The flask is then carefully filled to the graduation mark with deionised water.

The number of significant figures tells us how accurately we know the concentration of the solution. For example, a solution of $0\cdot0010$ mol l^{-1} has two significant figures (but four decimal places) and its concentration has been determined more accurately than a solution of $0\cdot001$ mol l^{-1}, which only has one significant figure (but three decimal places).

Significant figures

A quick guide to significant figures is given below:

- non-zero numbers are always significant, e.g. $1\cdot234$ g has 4 significant figures and $1\cdot2$ g has 2 significant figures.

- zeros that are between non-zero numbers are always significant, e.g. 6007 kg has 4 significant figures and $5\cdot08$ cm^3 has 3 significant figures.

- zeros to the left of the first non-zero number are not significant, e.g. $0\cdot005$ m has 1 significant figure and $0\cdot321$ cm has 3 significant figures.

- zeros at the end of a number are always significant if the number contains a decimal point, e.g. $210\cdot0$ nm has 4 significant figures and $0\cdot0600$ mol l^{-1} has 3 significant figures.

- zeros at the end of a number may or may not be significant if the number does not contain a decimal point, e.g. does 200 g have 1, 2 or 3 significant figures? It is impossible to decide without further information about how the measurement was made. Suppose a balance measuring to the nearest 10 g was used then the number would have 2 significant figures but if a balance measuring to the nearest 1 g was used then the number would have 3 significant figures. Quoting a number in scientific notation removes all doubt, e.g. $2\cdot0 \times 10^2$ g has 2 significant figures and implies that a balance reading to ±10 g had been used.

DON'T FORGET

A standard solution is a solution of accurately known concentration.

ONLINE TEST

Test your knowledge of significant figures at www.brightredbooks.net

contd

CALCULATIONS AND DILUTIONS

It may be necessary to calculate the required volume of stock solution needed to make a diluted solution of the desired concentration. For example, if 50 cm³ of 0·000040 mol l⁻¹ potassium permanganate is required, then it can be calculated that 2·0 cm³ of 0·0010 mol l⁻¹ of stock solution is needed as shown below.

First, the number of moles of potassium permanganate in the diluted solution must be determined:

Number of moles = concentration of diluted solution × volume of diluted solution

$$= 0.000040 \times 0.050$$

$$= 2.0 \times 10^{-6}$$

It is now possible to calculate the volume of stock solution that contains this number of moles.

Volume of stock solution = (number of moles needed) ÷ (concentration of stock solution)

$$= \frac{2.0 \times 10^{-6}}{0.0010} = 0.0020 \text{ litres} = 2.0 \text{ cm}^3$$

A simpler method combines these two steps and uses the expression $c_1 V_1 = c_2 V_2$, where c_1 and V_1 are the concentration and volume of the stock solution and c_2 and V_2 are the concentration and volume of the diluted solution. Therefore

$$V_1 = \frac{c_2 V_2}{c_1} = \frac{0.000040 \times 0.050}{0.0010}$$

$$= 0.0020 \text{ litres}$$

$$= 2.0 \text{ cm}^3$$

A 2·0 cm³ volume of 0·0010 mol l⁻¹ can be accurately measured using either a 2 cm³ pipette or a burette and transferred to a 50 cm³ volumetric flask and made up to the mark with distilled water.

 ## THINGS TO DO AND THINK ABOUT

Concentrations of solutions can be expressed in units other than mol l⁻¹. For example, the concentration of medicines is often given in mg/ml. The table below gives information about some other common concentration units.

Unit	Meaning	Useful conversion
mg/ml	milligrams per millilitre	milligrams of solute per millilitre of solvent
ppm	parts per million	milligrams of solute per litre of solvent
		or
		milligrams of substance per kilogram of solid
% w/v	% mass by volume	mass of solute per 100 ml of solvent
% v/v	% volume by volume	volume of solute per 100 ml of solvent

The dilution equation, $c_1 V_1 = c_2 V_2$, can be used even when the concentration of a solution is not given in mol l⁻¹.

For example, a pharmacist was asked to prepare 30·0 ml of a solution of cetirizine hydrochloride (an antihistamine medicine) with a concentration of 5·0 mg/ml. The stock solution of cetirizine hydrochloride was 75·0 mg/ml. Calculate the volume of stock solution needed to prepare the diluted medicine.

Using the equation $c_1 V_1 = c_2 V_2$, we can solve for V_2:

$$V_2 = \frac{c_1 V_1}{c_2} = \frac{5.0 \times 30.0}{75.0} = 2.0 \text{ ml}$$

ONLINE

Check out the video showing dilution at www. brightredbooks.net

ONLINE TEST

Revise calculating volumes and concentrations of standard solutions at www. brightredbooks.net

DON'T FORGET

Remember that the relationship $c_1 V_1 = c_2 V_2$ is very useful when calculating the volume or concentration of the stock solution needed to prepare a more dilute solution accurately.

DON'T FORGET

The unit 'ppm' can also be used to refer to 1 mg of a solute per 1 kg of solvent.

PRACTICAL SKILLS AND TECHNIQUES 2

COLORIMETRY

Colorimetry can be used to determine the concentration of coloured substances in solution. A colorimeter essentially consists of a light source, a coloured filter, a light detector and a recorder. The filter chosen is the complementary colour to the solution as this will result in the maximum absorbance. The light passes through the filter and then through the coloured solution. The difference in absorbance between the coloured solution and water is detected and noted as an absorbance value. Colorimetry uses the relationship between the intensity of the colour of the solution and the concentration. The more concentrated the solution, the greater the absorbance of light.

When using colorimetry, it is necessary to first prepare a **calibration graph**. Solutions of various concentrations are prepared and their absorbance values are recorded. The results are plotted on a graph of absorbance against concentration, similar to that shown here.

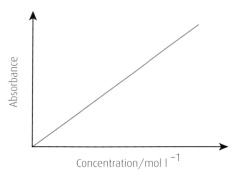

The calibration graph can be used to determine the concentration of the test sample. A solution of the sample being analysed is placed in the colorimeter and the absorbance reading is noted. This value can then be used to determine the concentration using a calibration graph. In an experiment to determine the percentage by mass of manganese in a steel paper clip, the manganese in the paper clip is first converted into Mn^{2+} ions by reacting the paper clip with nitric acid. Further oxidation using acidified potassium periodate produces purple permanganate ions (MnO_4^-). The resulting solution, plus rinsings, is added to a standard flask and made up to the graduation mark. The absorbance of the final solution is measured and the concentration of the permanganate ions determined from a calibration graph.

Points of good practice

- The calibration graph should cover the dilution range likely to be used in the determination of the concentration of the unknown solution. If the solution of unknown concentration has an absorbance value outwith those used in the calibration graph, another calibration graph should be prepared using more appropriate concentrations of the standard solutions.

- The absorbance values of the standard solutions should be measured at least twice and a mean value taken for the absorbance at each concentration. Rogue results (any that vary greatly from the best-fit line) should be discarded.

- Calibration graphs must be drawn as best-fit straight lines.

contd

The calibration graph can give an indication of the accuracy of the results obtained. If all the data points on the graph lie close to or on the best-fit line, it can be assumed that the determined concentration of the unknown solution is reasonably accurate. If, on the other hand, the data points are scattered around the best-fit line, the value obtained for the concentration of the unknown solution is likely to be inaccurate.

 ## THINGS TO DO AND THINK ABOUT

A student carried out an experiment to determine the percentage of manganese in a steel paper clip. A paper clip weighing 0·24 g was reacted and the manganese converted into purple permanganate ions. The reaction mixture was made up to 100 cm³ in a standard flask. The following calibration graph was prepared using dilutions of a stock solution of potassium permanganate.

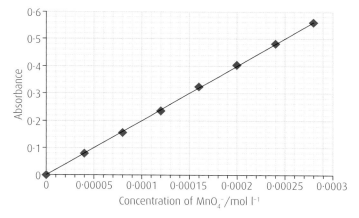

1 The absorbance of the solution was found to be 0·36. Using the calibration graph, determine the concentration of permanganate ions in the solution.

2 Calculate the percentage by mass of manganese in the steel paper clip.

TECHNIQUES USED IN THE PREPARATION AND PURIFICATION OF COMPOUNDS 1

The techniques listed below are often used as part of the synthesis and/or analysis of compounds:

- refluxing
- recrystallisation
- vacuum filtration
- distillation
- solvent extraction/use of a separating funnel

- determination of percentage yield
- determination of melting point and mixed melting point
- use of thin-layer chromatography to assess product purity

Most synthesis reactions will result in an impure product being formed as part of the reaction mixture. Impurities can include those present in the original starting materials (the reactants), unreacted reactants and the products formed in side reactions. It is usually necessary to remove the impurities from the desired product. There are a number of techniques that can be used to isolate and purify a desired product from a reaction mixture.

The pure products will often need to be analysed to either confirm their identity or to assess their purity.

You may carry out all of these techniques during one experiment. An example that uses many of these techniques is the alkaline hydrolysis of the ester ethyl benzoate to produce benzoic acid.

REFLUXING

The alkaline hydrolysis of ethyl benzoate is carried out by **refluxing** a known, accurate mass of ethyl benzoate with sodium hydroxide solution. The overall equation for the reaction is:

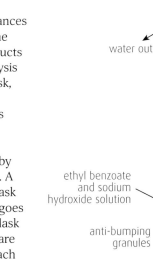

Refluxing is a technique that allows substances to be heated for a prolonged period of time without the volatile reactants and/or products escaping into the atmosphere. The hydrolysis mixture is placed in a round-bottomed flask, along with some anti-bumping granules. When a reaction mixture is heated, there is a tendency for it to boil violently as large bubbles of superheated vapour suddenly erupt from the mixture. This is prevented by the addition of the anti-bumping granules. A condenser is placed in the mouth of the flask and connected to a cold-water tap (water goes in at the bottom and out at the top). The flask is then heated and the vapours produced are condensed back into liquids when they reach the cool condenser.

water out

water in

ethyl benzoate and sodium hydroxide solution

anti-bumping granules

heat

Equipment used in a reflux experiment.

DON'T FORGET

Refluxing allows a reaction mixture to be heated for some time without any of the volatile substances escaping from the apparatus

VIDEO LINK

Watch the video clip showing reflux at www. brightredbooks.net

RECRYSTALLISATION

Recrystallisation is a technique used to purify an impure solid. You may have used this technique to purify an impure sample of benzoic acid.

The first step is to dissolve the impure solid in the minimum volume of an appropriate solvent. A small volume of hot solvent (water) is added to the impure solid (benzoic acid) and the mixture is heated. If the solid does not fully dissolve, more solvent is added. This process continues until all the solid has dissolved.

The solvent is chosen so that the desired product is readily soluble in it at high temperatures, but only sparingly soluble at lower temperatures so that crystals form as the hot mixture cools down. The solvent used to recrystallise benzoic acid is water.

Any insoluble impurities are removed by filtration. This is usually carried out as hot filtration. The filter funnel and conical flask used in the filtration are heated before use. This prevents the solvent mixture from cooling prematurely and forming crystals on both the filter paper and in the stem of the funnel.

The filtrate is now a hot saturated solution of the product and a dilute solution of impurities. As the solution cools down, the product crystallises out (it is less soluble at lower temperatures) and the impurities remain dissolved in the solvent. Once crystallisation is complete, the mixture is filtered.

VACUUM FILTRATION

Vacuum filtration involves carrying out filtration under reduced pressure and provides a faster method of separating a precipitate from a filtrate than traditional gravity filtration methods. A Büchner, Hirsch or sintered glass funnel can be used during vacuum filtration.

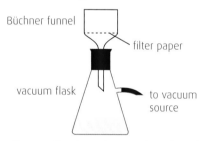

Büchner funnel

filter paper

vacuum flask

to vacuum source

Vacuum filtration using a Büchner funnel.

The pure recrystallised solid product collects on the filter paper. The filtrate contains a solution of soluble impurities. The solid product should now be washed with a small volume of cold solvent. This removes any soluble impurities that are mixed in with the pure solid.

The pure solid can be dried and weighed. A **percentage yield** can be calculated from its mass. The pure solid will often be subjected to analysis by **melting point** and **thin-layer chromatography** (see pp. 94–95).

THINGS TO DO AND THINK ABOUT

In a synthesis reaction, an impure sample of aspirin was prepared from 2-hydroxybenzoic acid and ethanoic anhydride. The reaction mixture was heated for approximately 10 minutes.

1. Suggest why reflux was not used during this reaction.

2. The impure aspirin sample was then purified by recrystallisation from ethanol. Describe the steps the chemist would need to take to purify the aspirin sample using this technique.

3. Ethanol was used as the solvent to recrystallise aspirin. Suggest why ethanol is a good choice of solvent.

VIDEO LINK

Check out the video clip showing recrystallisation at www.brightredbooks.net

VIDEO LINK

Head to www.brightredbooks.net for a video clip showing hot filtration.

DON'T FORGET

Recrystallisation is used to purify impure solids from a solvent in which the solid is soluble at high temperatures, but virtually insoluble at lower temperatures.

ONLINE

Watch the video clip of vacuum filtration at www.brightredbooks.net

ONLINE TEST

Test your knowledge of reflux, recrystallisation and vacuum filtration at www.brightredbooks.net

TECHNIQUES USED IN THE PREPARATION AND PURIFICATION OF COMPOUNDS 2

DISTILLATION

Distillation is the process of heating a liquid, or a mixture of liquids, until boiling and then collecting and cooling the resultant vapours. The diagram shows how distillation can be carried out in a laboratory.

Distillation can be used to purify a compound by separating it from less volatile substances in a reaction mixture. You may have used this technique to prepare cyclohexene from cyclohexanol. In this reaction, cyclohexanol is mixed with concentrated phosphoric acid and an elimination reaction takes place.

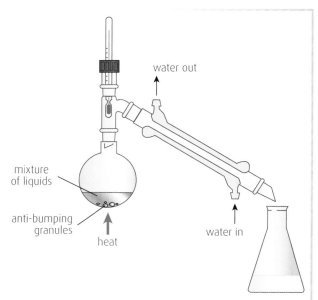

Equipment used in distillation.

The reaction mixture is slowly heated using the apparatus shown. Cyclohexene has a lower boiling point (83°C) than cyclohexanol (160°C) and so will vaporise first and rise up through the apparatus. The temperature of the vapour is noted and, as the vapour passes through the condenser, it condenses to a liquid and is collected in the conical flask. The cyclohexanol remains in the round-bottomed flask. The cyclohexene distillate is then further purified by **solvent extraction**.

Cyclohexanol is dehydrated to produce cyclohexene.

Distillation can also be used to identify compounds because the boiling point of a compound is a well-defined physical property. Boiling points do vary significantly with atmospheric pressure, however, and therefore the pressure must be controlled when identifying compounds using distillation.

SOLVENT EXTRACTION

In many organic syntheses, the crude product is extracted from the reaction mixture by **solvent extraction**. The 'crude product' is the name given to the mixture left over after a reaction. It contains the desired product as well as impurities such as unreacted reactants and products of side reactions.

Solvent extraction relies on the solute (crude product) being more soluble in a chosen solvent than it is in the original mixture. A suitable solvent must also be immiscible with the original mixture (often water-based). To extract the solute the solvent needs to be evaporated and so care must be taken when choosing a solvent for extraction that can be readily evaporated. In addition, the solvent must not react with the compound being extracted.

contd

After the reaction has taken place, the crude organic product is placed in a separating funnel and an organic solvent (immiscible in water) is added. The organic solvent is usually less dense than the water-based reaction mixture (unless the organic solvent is chlorinated) and so will form the upper layer in the funnel.

The product of the reaction will mostly dissolve in the organic solvent and this can be achieved by shaking the separating funnel. However, care should be taken when shaking the separating funnel as the gas pressure will build up. The pressure should be released occasionally by holding the funnel upside down and opening the tap.

The layers in the funnel are allowed to separate and the lower aqueous layer is removed by opening the tap. The tap is closed once the interface between the two layers gets close to the tap opening. The top organic layer is then drained into a second flask and stored. Some of the product will have remained dissolved in the water-based reaction mixture. In fact, an equilibrium will have established between the two layers.

Product (in aqueous reaction mixture) $\rightleftharpoons$ Product (in organic solvent)

The equilibrium may be such that 70% of the product is extracted into the organic solvent. This means that 30% of the product will remain in the aqueous layer. To extract more of the product, the aqueous layer must be extracted with another volume of organic solvent. Therefore the aqueous layer is returned to the separating funnel and a fresh volume of organic solvent is used to extract 70% of the remaining 30% of the product. Usually this process will be repeated two or three times to maximise the yield of the product. The organic solvent layer is sometimes washed with a fresh volume of water to ensure that as many impurities as possible are removed from the organic solvent layer.

In preparing cyclohexene from cyclohexanol, the impure cyclohexene obtained during the distillation of the reaction mixture can be further purified by solvent extraction. This can be done by adding the crude cyclohexene to a separating funnel along with an equal volume of sodium chloride solution. Impurities in the cyclohexene are extracted into the lower aqueous sodium chloride layer. The cyclohexene layer is then run off and treated with anhydrous magnesium sulfate to remove any remaining water.

Any product dissolved in an organic solvent is usually treated with an anhydrous salt such as anhydrous magnesium sulfate. Any water remaining in the organic solvent is absorbed by the anhydrous substance, which can then be removed by vacuum or gravity filtration.

Equipment used in solvent extraction.

VIDEO LINK

Check out the video clip of solvent extraction at www.brightredbooks.net

VIDEO LINK

Watch the animation explaining the theory of solvent extraction at www.brightredbooks.net

ONLINE TEST

Test your knowledge of distillation and solvent extraction at www.brightredbooks.net

 ## THINGS TO DO AND THINK ABOUT

Caffeine can be extracted from coffee and tea using solvent extraction. A tea solution was mixed with the solvent ethyl ethanoate in a separating funnel and the funnel was shaken. The layers were left to settle and the lower aqueous layer was then removed and the ethyl ethanoate layer was drained and stored.

1 Explain why the aqueous layer is then returned to the separating funnel and shaken with a further volume of ethyl ethanoate.

2 Why is it necessary to use a drying agent?

3 The drying agent was removed by filtration. Describe how caffeine could then be extracted from the ethyl ethanoate solvent.

TECHNIQUES USED IN ANALYSING COMPOUNDS

Once a product from a reaction has been isolated and purified, it is usually then analysed. Analysis can take many forms – often methods such as those described in the section on the determination of structure (pp. 72–77) are used to confirm that the correct product has been synthesised. Analysis can also be used to determine whether the product is pure. A number of other techniques are also routinely used.

DETERMINATION OF PERCENTAGE YIELD

It is useful for a chemist to know the percentage yield of the desired product. A very low yield indicates that the reaction has not been successful and that changes are needed before the reaction is repeated.

Example:

Calculating the percentage yield of benzoic acid
On p. 90 we looked at the hydrolysis reaction of ethyl benzoate to produce benzoic acid. The overall equation for this reaction is:

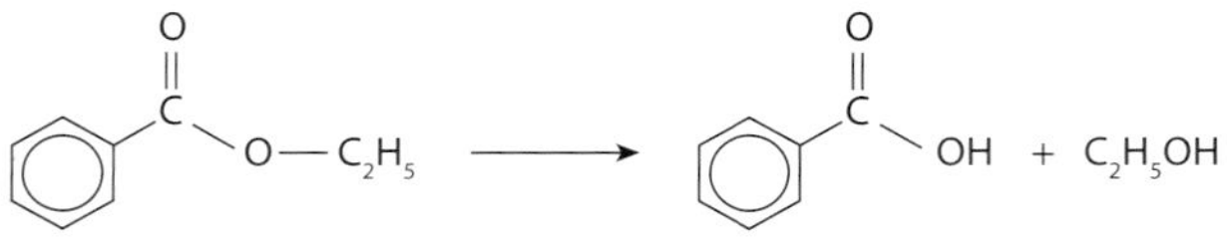

Based on the accurate mass of ethyl benzoate used in the experiment, the exact number of moles of ethyl benzoate can be calculated. The mole ratio for the reaction (1 : 1 in this example) then allows the theoretical number of moles, and therefore the theoretical mass of benzoic acid, to be determined:

$$\% \text{ yield} = \frac{\text{Actual yield}}{\text{Theoretical yield}} \times 100$$

Assuming that 5·36 g of ethyl benzoate were used in the experiment and that 3·24 g of benzoic acid were obtained, the percentage yield of benzoic acid can be calculated as:

1 mol ethyl benzoate → 1 mol benzoic acid

150·0 g → 122·0 g

5·36 g → $\frac{122·0}{150·0} \times 5·36 = 4·36$ g

$\% \text{ yield} = \frac{3·24}{4·36} \times 100 = 74\%$

Percentage yields will always be less than 100%. Losses in mass occur through the transfer of the product from one flask to another and purification by recrystallisation results in some product remaining in the solution. A large reduction in yields can be due to side reactions occurring, incomplete reactions, position of equilibrium and sometimes impure reactants.

DON'T FORGET

Impurities will lower the melting point and broaden the temperature range of melting.

VIDEO LINK

Head to www. brightredbooks.net and watch the video clip of melting point analysis.

MELTING POINT ANALYSIS

The identity of a pure product can be confirmed by **melting point** analysis.

Pure solids have defined melting points that fall within a narrow temperature range (the temperature difference between the start and end of melting). Unlike boiling points, melting points are not significantly affected by atmospheric pressure. If the melting point of the product from a reaction matches the literature value for that compound, then there is a high probability that the correct product has been made. To be completely sure, a mixed melting point experiment should be carried out.

A mixed melting point experiment involves mixing a little of the product with some 'pure' compound. In carrying out a mixed melting point experiment for the benzoic acid obtained by the hydrolysis of ethyl benzoate, some crystals of the laboratory-synthesised benzoic acid are mixed with pure benzoic acid. If the two compounds are identical, then a melting point of the correct temperature range will be obtained. If the melting point is lower than expected, then it is likely that the product is either impure or is not benzoic acid.

THIN-LAYER CHROMATOGRAPHY

Chromatography is a common technique used to separate mixtures of substances. There are many different types of chromatography and they all work in the same way. All have a **stationary phase** and a **mobile phase**.

Thin-layer chromatography (TLC) is often used as a faster alternative to paper chromatography. Instead of paper, a thin layer of silica gel or alumina coated onto glass, metal or plastic is used. The water held on the silica gel or alumina is the stationary phase. The mobile phase is a suitable solvent or a mixture of solvents. The solvent flows through the stationary phase and carries the components of the mixture with it. Different components in the mixture travel across the stationary phase at different rates.

As the solvent begins to soak up the chromatography plate, it first dissolves the compounds in the spot that has been placed on the base line. The compounds present will then be carried up the chromatography plate as the solvent continues to move upwards. How fast the components of a mixture are carried up the plate is determined by (1) how soluble the component is in the solvent and (2) how much the component adheres to the stationary phase. An equilibrium is established in which the components partition themselves between the stationary phase and the mobile phase in a fixed ratio.

TLC can be used to assess the purity of a compound – pure substances will show as one spot. The presence of more than one spot indicates the presence of impurities.

TLC can also be used to help determine the identity of a substance. There are two ways this can be achieved.

The first method makes use of R_f values, where $R_f = \dfrac{\text{distance travelled by sample}}{\text{distance travelled by solvent}}$.

In the chromatogram shown here, the R_f value is calculated as the distance $\frac{b}{a}$. Assuming that similar conditions are used to produce the chromatogram (temperature, solvent system, saturation levels), then the R_f values for different compounds can be compared directly.

The second method is when TLC is used to compare an unknown substance with the pure substance. For example, an aspirin sample prepared in the laboratory could be compared with a pure sample of aspirin. Three spots are made on the baseline of the TLC plate: one of the laboratory-prepared aspirin, a second of a sample of pure acetyl salicylic acid, and a third of a sample of both the laboratory and the pure samples (a **co-spot**). Once the plate has been developed, analysis is carried out by comparison. If the co-spot shows only one spot, it can be concluded that the laboratory-synthesised sample is exactly the same compound as the pure substance.

In chromatogram A, the co-spot mixture produced a single spot when developed. This shows that the product made was almost certainly aspirin. In chromatogram B, the co-spot produced two spots. This highlights that the product of the reaction was not aspirin.

ONLINE TEST

Test yourself on % yield, melting point and thin-layer chromatography at www.brightredbooks.net

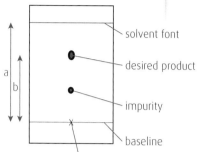

solvent font
desired product
impurity
baseline

mixture applied to this mark
Principles of thin-layer chromatography.

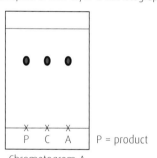

P C A   P = product

Chromatogram A

C = co-spot (product + aspirin)

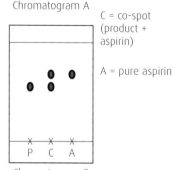

A = pure aspirin

P C A

Chromatogram B

Determination of the purity of aspirin by chromatography.

THINGS TO DO AND THINK ABOUT

Aspirin can be made by reacting 2-hydroxybenzoic acid with ethanoic anhydride as follows:

COOH   H₃C—C=O   COOH
   OH + O   →   O—C—CH₃ + CH₃COOH
         H₃C—C=O   ‖
                                      O

2-hydroxybenzoic   ethanoic   aspirin
acid   anhydride

The melting point of the aspirin produced was 129–133°C.

1 If 5·06 g of 2-hydroxybenzoic acid produced 3·20 g of aspirin, calculate the percentage yield for the reaction.

2 Describe how the technique of TLC could be used to show that the reaction had been successful.

3 The accepted value for the melting point of aspirin is 137°C. What do the melting points obtained for the sample of aspirin prepared in this experiment tell us?

4 Suggest a technique that could be used to purify the aspirin prepared in this experiment.

DON'T FORGET

TLC can be used to identify a compound by comparing the R_f values with those of known compounds. TLC can also be used to assess the purity of a compound as a pure compound will give only one spot on the developed chromatogram.

VIDEO LINK

Check out the video clip showing TLC at www.brightredbooks.net

PROJECT 1

DON'T FORGET

You can get up to 30 marks for your Project Report.

ONLINE

You will find some ideas on possible projects at www. brightredbooks.net

HOW MANY MARKS FOR THE PROJECT?

The exam is marked out of 100, but in Advanced Higher Chemistry you also carry out a project. You have to write up a Project Report, which is marked externally by an SQA marker and is also quality assured by the SQA. The Project Report is worth 30 marks and so the total number of marks is 130. Your Project Report should be between 2500 and 4500 words long. You have to submit the word count with your Project Report – you must keep your word count below 4950 or you will incur a penalty of 3 marks.

GETTING STARTED

This is an opportunity for you to carry out a piece of independent research on a topic that interests you. It may be something you have covered in Advanced Higher Chemistry this session, or something that you covered at Higher or earlier years, or it may be a topic you have read about on the internet or from other media sources. You may find that scientific journals such as *School Science Review*, *New Scientist* and *Scientific American* are useful in helping you to choose a topic for your project.

However, your best source of ideas is your chemistry teacher or lecturer, as he or she will know which investigations or projects have been successful at your centre in previous sessions. They will also know what apparatus and chemicals are available to you.

It is important that you are not over-ambitious. Your project is unlikely to be a piece of original research, but it will be new to you. Take the advice given by your teacher or lecturer. You have only a limited time available to plan your project, carry out the experimental work and then write up the Project Report. If you try to do too much, you may run out of time.

After you have identified a suitable topic and agreed this with your teacher or lecturer, you will have to decide the main aims of the project and how you are going to meet these aims. You will need to answer questions such as:

- Which experiments will I carry out?

- What apparatus will I need?

- Which chemicals will I need?

- How much of each chemical will I need?

- What precautions will I need to take?

- What concentrations of solutions will I need?

You will have to keep a record of all your plans. This will include your initial aims and plans. You may have to carry out some initial experimental trials and then make amendments to your initial plan. This may take some time, but is good practice. Your record should include any changes to your initial aims and plans and the reasons for making these changes.

You will also need to carry out and produce a full written risk assessment before you start any experimental work. You will need to work out how you can minimise the risks to yourself and others. The options for doing this may include using control measures such as working in a fume cupboard, wearing gloves, using smaller quantities of reagents, finding alternative, safer chemicals, or finding an alternative, safer procedure. Again, your teacher or lecturer should be able to give you good advice and you should not proceed without their agreement. You should also make a brief record of all the discussions you have had with your teacher or lecturer and what decisions you have made. It is good practice to ask your teacher to sign and date all the decisions that have been agreed upon.

contd

You should always check with your teacher or lecturer the first time you carry out any procedure or use any piece of equipment you have not used before. It will be your responsibility to collect the materials you need for your project and to put them away when you have finished with them.

Your record of work, which may be paper-based or electronic, may be presented as your evidence for a record of experimental data. In this regard, you must record all your raw results and the uncertainties associated with each measurement. If you tabulate your results, the tables should have proper headings and the appropriate units. The more information you record as you carry out your project, then the easier it will be to write up a good, comprehensive Project Report later. The number of marks you obtain out of the 30 marks available for the project will be awarded by the marker based purely on what he or she reads in your Project Report.

Chemical suppliers send material safety data sheets to centres when chemicals are purchased, so you should ask your teacher or lecturer to see these when you are preparing your risk assessment.

DON'T FORGET

You must carry out a full risk assessment before you start any experimental work for your project. You should also ask your teacher or lecturer to sign and date your record of work where you have noted your experimental results.

DON'T FORGET

You should use your record of work to record your aims, planning, risk assessments, observations and the results of your research. You should also ask your teacher or lecturer to write appropriate comments and advice there as well.

HOW YOUR PROJECT REPORT WILL BE MARKED

Your Project Report should be easy to follow. You will start off with a title page, followed by a contents page. The contents page must show the page numbers and therefore the pages throughout your report must be numbered.

The marking is subdivided into categories as follows:

- Abstract (one mark)
- Introduction (four marks)
- Procedures (nine marks)
- Results (six marks)
- Discussion, Conclusion(s) and Evaluation (eight marks)
- Presentation (two marks)

Total = 30 marks

You will find more information about how these marks are allocated in the next section. Read these pages carefully and try to ensure that all the points are covered in your Project Report before it is submitted to the SQA.

ALLOCATION OF MARKS IN THE PROJECT

Abstract (one mark)

To gain this mark you have to write a brief abstract, which is a summary stating the overall aim(s) and finding(s) of your project. This should be on a fresh page and must immediately follow the contents page and under a separate heading. It must be placed before the Introduction. The overall findings given here must relate to the aim(s) of your project and must be consistent with the conclusion(s) given near the end of your Project Report.

Introduction (four marks)

The Introduction should be on a new page starting immediately after the abstract. This is an opportunity for you to show how much you know about the background chemistry to your project. You should take this opportunity to write down any formulae, including structural formulae, and balanced chemical equations, including ion–electron equations and the overall redox equations where relevant. You should also describe and explain any chemical ideas and principles behind your investigation. You can add some historical or background information if you wish, but remember this category is marked on chemical information only and you must try restrict your report to fewer than 3000 words. The marker will use his or her professional judgement to decide whether your Introduction is of an A grade standard (four marks), right down to whether it is only worth one mark, or perhaps even no marks at all if there is no chemistry present, or if the chemistry you have given is wrong. You should try to use your own words wherever possible and try to avoid copying directly from the internet or any other source. It is acceptable to copy diagrams directly from the internet, but you should state where these have come from by including information about them in your reference list.

Procedures (nine marks)

The procedures you adopt must be appropriate to the aims of your project – if they are, then you will be awarded one mark.

You can gain up to another two marks for describing the procedures you used in sufficient detail to allow your project to be repeated using only the information given in your report. You should also ensure that your report is written up in the past tense and using the impersonal voice. For example, 'a titration was carried out' is correct, but 'I carried out a titration' is not acceptable. You must not write up your procedure(s) as a list of bullet point instructions. The marker will be looking for details such as the concentrations of solutions used, temperatures and quantities, so that another competent Advanced Higher Chemistry student would be able to repeat your experiments.

You have to illustrate that the procedure(s) you have used are at an appropriate level for Advanced Higher Chemistry. Even if you are doing a project on a topic you first met at Higher or earlier, the treatment of the topic must be at Advanced Higher level. If your procedure involves volumetric analysis, gravimetric analysis, chromatography, or any other technique studied in Advanced Higher Chemistry, you should get at least one mark here. A further mark may be awarded if your report demonstrates that you have carried out more than one technique, have carried out a control experiment (see page 85), standardised solutions or have carried out a modification in the light of experience as you carried out your experimental work. An example of a valid modification would be having to change the concentration of one or more solutions, or to change a solvent. If you have carried out a modification to improve your results, then you need to explain fully why the modification was needed. A good way to do this is to give the results before and after the modification. You can gain a maximum of two marks here.

To increase the reliability of your results, you need to repeat your experiments with fresh samples to obtain duplicate results. Ideally, these duplicate results will be close to the original results and you can then take a mean value. You may wish to discuss the reliability and precision in the evaluation of your project. If the duplicate and original results are very different, then you should repeat the procedure again to obtain more results. You should also discard any rogue results you find when doing calculations. One mark is awarded here.

There is also a mark awarded for the accuracy of the measurements in your procedures. You need to make sure you are using the correct apparatus and that you have weighed the reagents accurately to the appropriate number of decimal places corresponding to the balance used.

The final two marks awarded in this category are for your risk assessment. You have to show that you have taken the appropriate safety measures and that you are aware of the hazards associated with the chemicals and experimental procedures used and you must describe what you have done to minimise these risks. Where no significant hazards are associated with the chemicals and/or the procedures then you must state this is the case and that no additional precautions were necessary.

contd

Results (six marks)

The marker will decide whether the results part of your Project Report are to be marked quantitatively or qualitatively to give you the benefit of the doubt with respect to the higher number of marks awarded.

In both cases you get one mark if your results are relevant to the procedures of your project.

You have to present your raw and processed results in a clear and concise manner using tables, graphs, diagrams and calculations, as appropriate. These should be clearly set out and have the correct headings, axes, labels and units. Take care to present your final results to the correct number of significant figures (see page 86 for further help with this).

You must also record detailed observations such as colour changes, the shape and colour of any crystals formed and other observations. The marker may be aware of the observations expected and you may not get the maximum number of marks here if you have omitted to record an expected observation.

Discussion (eight marks) – this includes conclusion and evaluation

You should make sure you write up an overall conclusion and evaluation here, even if you have done this after each experiment (not recommended). To gain maximum marks you must write an overall conclusion and evaluation at the end of your report.

For the first mark here you need to make sure that your conclusion(s) are valid from your results and relate to the aim(s) of your project.

There are six marks for your evaluation of your project. This is an opportunity for you to reflect in a positive way on what you did in your project and to suggest possible modifications or improvements that you could make if you were to start all over again.

Three marks are available for the evaluation of the procedures you used. To gain these marks you may wish to comment on the accuracy of your measurements, such as whether you carried out an adequate number of duplicate and control experiments, the sources of uncertainties with respect to the values of the measurements you took, and any modifications you made to the procedures.

Three marks are for the evaluation of your results. The marker will be looking for how well you have analysed and interpreted your results. You may wish to work out the effect on your final calculated results of all the uncertainties in your individual recorded measurements.

Your marker will decide whether you have covered the most important aspects of your evaluation before awarding marks in this category.

The last mark here is a bonus mark given for the quality of your project as a whole.

Presentation (two marks)

One mark here is for making sure that you have included a title page, contents page, page numbers and that your report is easy to follow.

The other mark is for the references. You have to cite at least three references in the main body of your report and list these cited references correctly at the end of your report. There are various acceptable standard forms of referencing and your teacher or lecturer will advise you on this. Your references can include books, journals or periodicals and websites.

DON'T FORGET

You need to put in as much chemistry as you can in the Introduction to gain all four marks.

DON'T FORGET

You need to carry out each experiment in duplicate to improve the reliability of your results.

DON'T FORGET

You must put in your raw results, so if you are carrying out titrations you must include all your initial and final burette readings.

ANSWERS

THINGS TO DO AND THINK ABOUT ANSWERS

INORGANIC AND PHYSICAL CHEMISTRY

Electromagnetic radiation and atomic spectra 2, pp. 8–9

Energy = 1313 kJ mol⁻¹. The value in the SQA Data Booklet is 1312 kJ mol⁻¹.

Energy = 1313 kJ mol^{-1}. The value in the SQA Data Booklet is 1312 kJ mol^{-1}.

Electromagnetic radiation and atomic spectra 3, pp. 10–11

1   Helium was discovered by using a spectroscope to look indirectly at the Sun. Lines that did not correspond to any known element were present in the spectrum and so a new element had been discovered. It was named helium after the Greek word for the Sun, 'Helios'.

2   $1{\cdot}0 \times 10^{-4}$ mol l^{-1}.

Atomic orbitals, electronic configurations and the Periodic Table 1, pp. 12–13

1   There will be two electrons in the s subshell, six electrons in the p subshell and 10 electrons in the d subshell, which means that there must be 14 electrons in the f subshell. Therefore there must be seven f orbitals to accommodate these 14 electrons.

2   In the fourth shell, there will be one 4s orbital, three 4p orbitals, five 4d orbitals and seven 4f orbitals. The values for n, l, m and s for all the electrons in a completely filled fourth shell are shown in the table:

Value of n	Value of l	Values of m	Type of orbital
4	0	0	s
4	1	−1, 0, +1	p
4	2	−2, −1, 0, +1, +2	d
4	3	−3, −2, −1, 0, +1, +2, +3	f

There will be two electrons per orbital. Each will have different spin quantum numbers (one electron in the orbital will have
$s = +\frac{1}{2}$ and the other electron will have $s = -\frac{1}{2}$).

Atomic orbitals, electronic configurations and the Periodic Table 2, pp. 14–15

1   D

2   a   He $1s^2$

   b   N $1s^2\ 2s^2\ 2p^3$

   c   Al^{3+} $1s^2\ 2s^2\ 2p^6$

   d   Ar $1s^2\ 2s^2\ 2p^6\ 3s^2\ 3p^6$

   e   Ca $1s^2\ 2s^2\ 2p^6\ 3s^2\ 3p^6\ 4s^2$

   f   Ca^{2+} $1s^2\ 2s^2\ 2p^6\ 3s^2\ 3p^6$

   g   Br$^-$ $1s^2\ 2s^2\ 2p^6\ 3s^2\ 3p^6\ 3d^{10}\ 4s^2\ 4p^6$

   h   S^{2-} $1s^2\ 2s^2\ 2p^6\ 3s^2\ 3p^6$

Atomic orbitals, electronic configurations and the Periodic Table 3, pp. 16–17

1   D

2   A   He $1s^2$

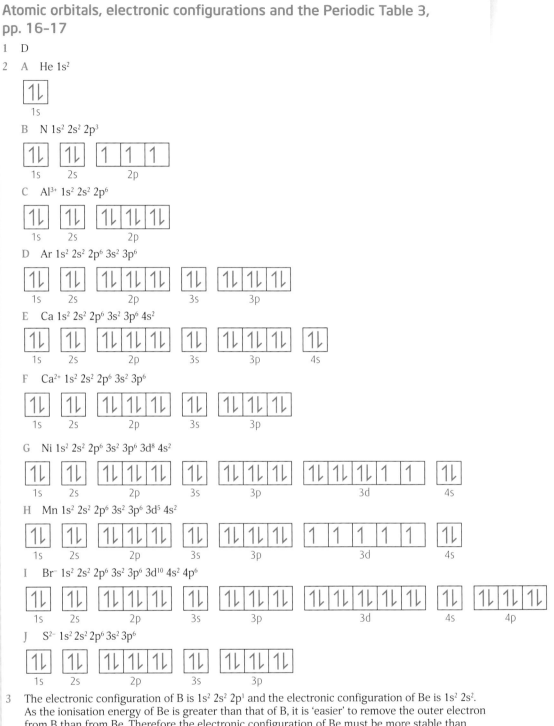

B   N $1s^2\, 2s^2\, 2p^3$

C Al^{3+} $1s^2\, 2s^2\, 2p^6$

D   Ar $1s^2\, 2s^2\, 2p^6\, 3s^2\, 3p^6$

E   Ca $1s^2\, 2s^2\, 2p^6\, 3s^2\, 3p^6\, 4s^2$

F Ca^{2+} $1s^2\, 2s^2\, 2p^6\, 3s^2\, 3p^6$

G   Ni $1s^2\, 2s^2\, 2p^6\, 3s^2\, 3p^6\, 3d^8\, 4s^2$

H   Mn $1s^2\, 2s^2\, 2p^6\, 3s^2\, 3p^6\, 3d^5\, 4s^2$

I Br^- $1s^2\, 2s^2\, 2p^6\, 3s^2\, 3p^6\, 3d^{10}\, 4s^2\, 4p^6$

J S^{2-} $1s^2\, 2s^2\, 2p^6\, 3s^2\, 3p^6$

3   The electronic configuration of B is $1s^2\, 2s^2\, 2p^1$ and the electronic configuration of Be is $1s^2\, 2s^2$. As the ionisation energy of Be is greater than that of B, it is 'easier' to remove the outer electron from B than from Be. Therefore the electronic configuration of Be must be more stable than that of B. This is because the electron to be removed from a Be atom is from a full 2s subshell. Full subshells are more stable, so more energy is required to remove this electron than is required to remove the electron from the outer shell of a boron atom. The electron in the outer shell of a boron atom is a single electron in a 2p subshell.

The electronic configuration of N is $1s^2\, 2s^2\, 2p^3$ and for O it is $1s^2\, 2s^2\, 2p^4$. If you write these in orbital box notation, you will see that the electron to be removed from N is from a half-full 2p subshell. As half-full subshells are also fairly stable, then more energy is required to remove an outer electron from N than from O. Therefore the first ionisation energy of N is slightly greater than that of O.

THINGS TO DO AND THINK ABOUT ANSWERS (CONT)

Shapes of molecules and polyatomic ions, pp. 18–19

a   Four bonding pairs, zero non-bonding pairs, so the shape is tetrahedral (like methane).

b   Three bonding pairs, one non-bonding pair, so shape is trigonal pyramidal (like ammonia).

c   Two bonding pairs, two non-bonding pairs, so shape is non-linear (like water).

d   Three bonding pairs, two non-bonding pairs, so molecule is shaped like the letter T.

e   Two bonding pairs, three non-bonding pairs, so shape is probably linear.

f   Five bonding pairs, one non-bonding pair, so shape is square pyramidal.

g

Four bonding pairs. Iodine is the central atom and has seven outer electrons. Each fluorine atom contributes one electron, giving a total of 11 electrons. The ion has a charge of −1 and therefore we must add one electron to give a total of 12 electrons, i.e. six pairs of electrons around the central I atom. These six pairs of electrons will space themselves out in an octahedral shape. However, of these six pairs, only four will be bonding pairs (there are four I–F bonds in IF_4^-) and so there must also be two non-bonding pairs. The shape of the IF_4^- ion is shown in the diagram. The two non-bonding pairs are at 180° because they produce the greatest repulsion. The four fluorine atoms are in a horizontal plane and at 90° to each other. This is a fairly unusual shape and is known as square planar.

Electronic configurations and oxidation states of transition metals, pp. 20–21

1   Scandium always forms Sc^{3+} ions and, because the 4s electrons are lost first, the electronic configuration of the Sc^{3+} ion is $1s^2\,2s^2\,2p^6\,3s^2\,3p^6$, so there are no electrons in the d subshell.

    Zinc always forms Zn^{2+} ions and the electronic configuration of the Zn^{2+} ion is $1s^2\,2s^2\,2p^6\,3s^2\,3p^6\,3d^{10}$ and it does not have an **incomplete d** subshell.

2   The electronic configuration for Fe^{2+} is $1s^2\,2s^2\,2p^6\,3s^2\,3p^6\,3d^6$ and for Fe^{3+} it is $1s^2\,2s^2\,2p^6\,3s^2\,3p^6\,3d^5$ in spectroscopic notation.

    In orbital box notation, considering only the d orbitals:

         Fe^{2+} Fe^{3+}

    There is a special stability associated with all the orbitals in the d subshell being half-filled and so Fe^{3+} is more stable than Fe^{2+}.

3   Oxidation number is six or (VI) and because Cr is in a high oxidation state, then $Cr_2O_7^{2-}$ is a good oxidising agent. When it acts as an oxidising agent, it is usually reduced to the Cr^{3+} ion.

Transition metal complexes 1, pp. 22–23

1   a   Tetrachlorocobaltate(II)

      b   hexaamminenickel(II)

      c   hexachloroplatinate(IV).

2   a $[Fe(CN)_6]^{3-}$

      b $[Ag(NH_3)_2]^+$

      c $[Cu(Cl)_4]^{2-}$.

Transition metal complexes 2, pp. 24–25

1   Chromium is in oxidation state (VI) in $Cr_2O_7^{2-}$. The electronic configuration of the chromium atom is $1s^2\,2s^2\,2p^6\,3s^2\,3p^6\,3d^5\,4s^1$ and so the electronic configuration of Cr(VI) is $1s^2\,2s^2\,2p^6\,3s^2\,3p^6$, which means that there are no electrons in the d subshell and so d–d transitions are not possible.

2 (i) The $[CoCl_4]^{2-}$ complex absorbs light mainly from the red and also partly from the orange region of the visible spectrum and this explains the blue–green or cyan colour of this complex in solution. The $[Co(H_2O)_6]^{2+}$ complex is pink in solution because it absorbs light mainly from the middle of the visible spectrum.

   (ii) The energy differences between the low energy d orbitals and the higher energy d orbitals will be different in the two complexes because of the different positions of the Cl⁻ and H_2O ligands in the spectrochemical series. Also the $[CoCl_4]^{2-}$ complex is tetrahedral and the $[Co(H_2O)_6]^{2+}$ complex is octahedral in shape; this also causes differences in the splitting of the d orbitals.

Chemical equilibrium 1: Introducing the equilibrium constant, K, pp. 26–27

1 a $K = [H^+(aq)][OH^-(aq)]$ (remember that $[H_2O(l)]$ is usually omitted from the expression for the equilibrium constant).

   b As K is increasing, the position of equilibrium must be shifting to the right-hand side as the temperature increases. Increasing the temperature always favours the endothermic reaction, so the forward reaction must be endothermic and the sign of ΔH^o must be positive.

Chemical equilibrium 2: K_w and the pH scale, pp. 28–29

1 D. If the pH has increased by two units, then the hydrogen ion concentration must have decreased by a factor of 100. Remember that the pH increases when $[H^+]$ decreases and that the pH scale is a logarithmic scale. You can also work it out by saying that when pH = 4, $[H^+] = 1 \times 10^{-4}$ mol l⁻¹ and when pH = 6, $[H^+] = 1 \times 10^{-6}$ mol l⁻¹ and so $[H^+]$ has decreased by a factor of 100.

2 A. Lemon juice has the lower pH and so has the greater $[H^+]$. As there is a difference of two pH units, then the increase in $[H^+]$ must be by a factor of 100.

3 a 0·66

   b 5·39

   c 9·07.

4 a 6×10^{-4} mol l⁻¹

   b 4×10^{-10} mol l⁻¹

   c $2 \cdot 6 \times 10^{-6}$ mol l⁻¹

   d $1 \cdot 1 \times 10^{-8}$ mol l⁻¹.

Chemical equilibrium 3: The concept of strong and weak, pp. 30–31

1 D. The stoichiometry of the reaction is the same for strong and weak bases.

2 C. Ammonia is a weak base and so is not completely ionised (dissociated). However, an aqueous solution of ammonia is alkaline and so contains more hydroxide ions than hydrogen ions.

Chemical equilibrium 4: Salts, pp. 32–33

1 The two equilibria referred to in the question are the equilibrium present in water and the equilibrium present in the propanoic acid solution.

   As the salt solution has a pH >7, it is the salt of a weak acid and strong base. The strong base is KOH and, as it is fully ionised, we cannot write an equilibrium equation for its dissociation.

   Propanoic acid is the weak acid and the equilibrium equation for its dissociation is:

   $CH_3CH_2COOH(aq) \rightleftharpoons CH_3CH_2COO^-(aq) + H^+(aq)$

   The equation showing the equilibrium present in water is:

   $H_2O(l) \rightleftharpoons H^+(aq) + OH^-(aq)$

   In both equations the position of equilibrium lies well over to the left-hand side, i.e. to the reactant side. When potassium propanoate dissolves in water, the propanoate ions react with the hydrogen ions from the water to form propanoic acid molecules. This effectively removes some of the $H^+(aq)$ ions and so there will be fewer hydrogen ions than hydroxide ions present and the solution is alkaline.

2 As potassium sorbate forms an alkaline solution in water, it is the salt of a weak acid and a strong base. Therefore sorbic acid must be a weak acid. (It is not necessary to know its formula or write an equation for its dissociation to be able to state that it must be a weak acid.)

Chemical equilibrium 5: K_a and the pH of weak acids, pp. 34–35

1 and 2

(i) $HCOOH(aq) + H_2O(l) \rightleftharpoons HCOO^-(aq) + H_3O^+(aq)$
conjugate base + conjugate acid

(ii) $CH_3COOH(aq) + H_2O(l) \rightleftharpoons CH_3COO^-(aq) + H_3O^+(aq)$
conjugate base + conjugate acid

(iii) $H_2SO_3(aq) + H_2O(l) \rightleftharpoons HSO_3^-(aq) + H_3O^+(aq)$
conjugate base + conjugate acid

3 To answer this question, you need to use the expression,
$pH = \frac{1}{2}pK_a - \frac{1}{2}\log_{10}c$: (i) 3·23; (ii) 3·60.

Chemical equilibrium 6: Buffers and indicators, pp. 36–37

1 For an indicator to be useful in detecting the end-point of an acid–base reaction, the pH range of the indicator must fit into the vertical part of the titration curve for that reaction. The vertical part of the titration curve will include the pH of the salt solution at the end-point.

a HCl is a strong acid and NaOH is a strong base and so any of these indicators could be used successfully.

b CH_3COOH is a weak acid and NaOH is a strong base and so the pH of the end-point will be >7 because the salt formed will be sodium ethanoate. Phenolphthalein has a pH range >7 and could be used to detect the end-point in this titration.

c HCl is a strong acid and NH_3 is a weak base and so the pH of the salt solution (ammonium chloride) at the end-point will be <7. Methyl red would be the most useful indicator in this titration, but bromocresol purple would also work.

2 Any soluble salt of propanoic acid and a strong base would be suitable. Acceptable answers include sodium propanoate or potassium propanoate.

3 The relevant equations are:
$HCOOH(aq) \rightleftharpoons HCOO^-(aq) + H^+(aq)$ and
$NaHCOO(s) \rightarrow Na^+(aq) + HCOO^-(aq)$

a When HCl(aq) is added, its H^+ ions react with the $HCOO^-$ ions from the sodium methanoate salt to form HCOOH molecules, so $[H^+]$ remains the same as before and the pH is unchanged.

b When NaOH(aq) is added, its OH^- ions react with the H^+ formed from the dissociation of methanoic acid. To compensate for this, more methanoic acid molecules dissociate to replace these H^+ ions and so, once again, $[H^+]$ remains the same as before and the pH is unchanged.

4 Using the expression, $pH = pK_a - \log\frac{[acid]}{[salt]}$, the pH is calculated to be 4·94.

To obtain this result, remember that 40 cm^3 of 0·1 mol l^{-1} ethanoic acid solution diluted to a total volume of 100 cm^3 becomes 0·04 mol l^{-1} and that 60 cm^3 of 0·1 mol l^{-1} sodium ethanoate solution diluted to a total volume of 100 cm^3 becomes 0·06 mol l^{-1}.

Reaction feasibility 1, pp. 38–39

1 -169 kJ mol^{-1}

2 a (i) ΔS^o +ve

(ii) ΔS^o −ve

(iii) ΔS^o approximately zero.

b $+25$ J K^{-1} mol^{-1}

Reaction feasibility 2, pp. 40–41

Equilibrium is reached when approximately 75% of R is converted into P.
Hence $K = \frac{[products]}{[reactants]} = \frac{75}{25} = 3$

Kinetics, pp. 42–43

1   $x = 2$ and $y = 0.50$.

2   12.

3   Order with respect to **A** = 1; order with respect to **B** = 1;
    Rate = $k[\mathbf{A}][\mathbf{B}]$.

ORGANIC CHEMISTRY AND INSTRUMENTAL ANALYSIS

Molecular structure, pp. 44–45

1   a $C_9H_8O_4$ b $C_9H_8O_4$

2   a   b   c   d   e

    f

3   a $H_3C–CH_3$ b    c $H_3C{-}O{-}CH_2{-}CH_3$ d

Molecular orbitals 1, pp. 46–47

1   a   18 b 5

2   One s orbital, three p orbitals and three d orbitals.

Molecular orbitals 3, pp. 50–51

a   Electromagnetic energy is absorbed when electrons move from a low energy level (HOMO) to a higher energy level (LUMO). The energy absorbed corresponds to the visible spectrum and the colour of the compound is complementary to that absorbed.

b   Molecule X absorbs orange light; molecule Y absorbs yellow light. Molecule X has a smaller HOMO–LUMO energy gap than molecule Y.

Synthesis 1: Bond fission, electrophiles and nucleophiles, pp. 54–55

1   a

    Br — Br → Br· + Br·

    b   H–Cl → H$^\oplus$ + :Cl$^\ominus$

2   a   The non-bonding electron pair or lone pair.

    b   **A** nucleophile; **B** electrophile; **C** nucleophile; and **D** nucleophile.

Synthesis 2: Haloalkanes, pp. 56–57

a

b $H_2C{=}C{-}CH_2{-}CH_3$ and $H_3C{-}C{=}CH{-}CH_3$

THINGS TO DO AND THINK ABOUT ANSWERS (CONT)

Synthesis 3: Mechanisms of nucleophilic substitution reactions pp. 58–59

If the mechanism was S_N2, then the OH^- ion nucleophile would have to attack the carbon atom of the C–Br bond from the side exactly **opposite** to that of the Br atom. You can see from the structure that access to this C atom is severely restricted, thus explaining why the compound is unlikely to react via an S_N2 mechanism.

Synthesis 5: Alkenes, pp. 62–63

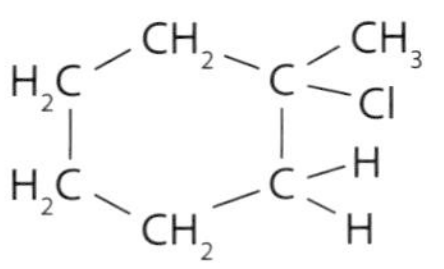

and

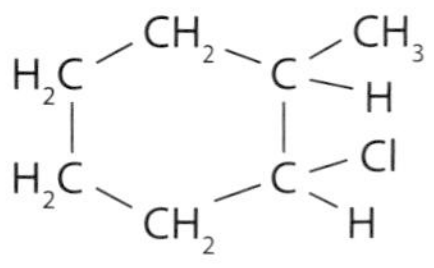

The major product is called 1-chloro-1-methylcyclohexane.

Synthesis 7: Carboxylic acids and amines, pp. 66–67

D, because $C_2H_5N(CH_3)_2$ is a tertiary amine.

Synthesis 8: Aromatic hydrocarbons, pp. 68–69

Graphite has a layer structure and each layer can be regarded as a network of fused benzene rings. The delocalised electrons extend over the whole layer and allow graphite to conduct electricity. The benzene molecule also contains delocalised electrons and this would imply that individual molecules would conduct electricity. However, a collection of benzene molecules, such as in a beaker of benzene liquid, does not conduct. This is because the delocalised electrons are confined to the individual benzene molecules and cannot 'jump' from one molecule to another.

Synthesis 9: Synthetic organic chemistry, pp. 70–71

a Step 1

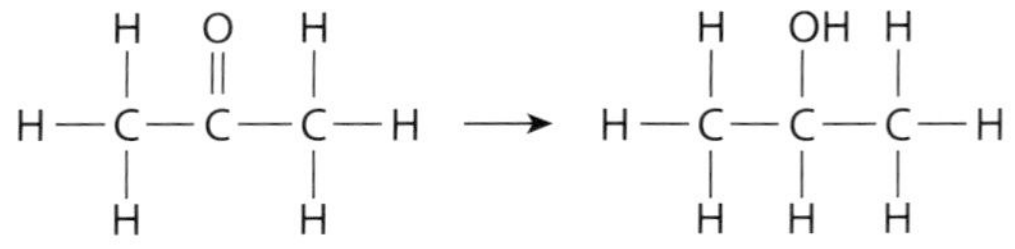

Propanone is reduced to propan-2-ol by heating the propanone with lithium aluminium hydride ($LiAlH_4$) in ether (ethoxyethane).

Step 2

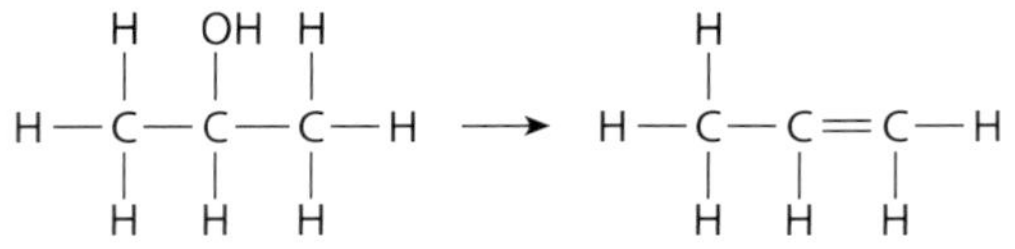

Propan-2-ol is heated with concentrated phosphoric acid and it undergoes an elimination reaction to form propene.

Step 3

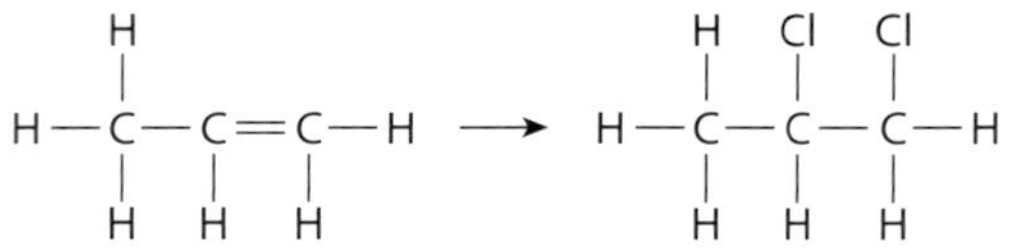

The propene is finally treated with chlorine solution and it undergoes an addition reaction to form the desired product, 1,2-dichloropropane.

b Step 1

$$H-\underset{\underset{H}{|}}{\overset{\overset{H}{|}}{C}}-\underset{\underset{H}{|}}{\overset{\overset{H}{|}}{C}}-C\overset{\diagup O}{\diagdown H} \longrightarrow H-\underset{\underset{H}{|}}{\overset{\overset{H}{|}}{C}}-\underset{\underset{H}{|}}{\overset{\overset{H}{|}}{C}}-C\overset{\diagup O}{\diagdown OH}$$

Some of the propanal is oxidised to propanoic acid by heating it with acidified potassium dichromate solution.

Step 2

$$H-\underset{\underset{H}{|}}{\overset{\overset{H}{|}}{C}}-\underset{\underset{H}{|}}{\overset{\overset{H}{|}}{C}}-C\overset{\diagup O}{\diagdown H} \longrightarrow H-\underset{\underset{H}{|}}{\overset{\overset{H}{|}}{C}}-\underset{\underset{H}{|}}{\overset{\overset{H}{|}}{C}}-\underset{\underset{H}{|}}{\overset{\overset{H}{|}}{C}}-OH$$

The rest of the propanal is reduced to propan-1-ol by heating the propanal with lithium aluminium hydride (LiAlH$_4$) in ether (ethoxyethane).

Step 3

$$H-\underset{\underset{H}{|}}{\overset{\overset{H}{|}}{C}}-\underset{\underset{H}{|}}{\overset{\overset{H}{|}}{C}}-C\overset{\diagup O}{\diagdown OH} \;+\; HO-\underset{\underset{H}{|}}{\overset{\overset{H}{|}}{C}}-\underset{\underset{H}{|}}{\overset{\overset{H}{|}}{C}}-\underset{\underset{H}{|}}{\overset{\overset{H}{|}}{C}}-H \;\rightleftharpoons\; H-\underset{\underset{H}{|}}{\overset{\overset{H}{|}}{C}}-\underset{\underset{H}{|}}{\overset{\overset{H}{|}}{C}}-\underset{\overset{\|}{O}}{C}-O-\underset{\underset{H}{|}}{\overset{\overset{H}{|}}{C}}-\underset{\underset{H}{|}}{\overset{\overset{H}{|}}{C}}-\underset{\underset{H}{|}}{\overset{\overset{H}{|}}{C}}-H \;+\; H_2O$$

A mixture of the propanoic acid and the propan-1-ol is heated in the presence of concentrated sulfuric acid (or concentrated phosphoric acid) as a catalyst to form the ester, propyl propanoate. This is a condensation reaction.

Experimental determination of structure 1, pp. 72–73

a Mass of oxygen = 100 − (40·00 + 6·71) = 53·29

	C	H	O
Mass (g)	40·00	6·71	53·29
Number of moles	$\frac{40\cdot00}{12}$ = 3·33	$\frac{6\cdot71}{1}$ = 6·71	$\frac{53\cdot29}{16}$ = 3·33
Mole ratio	1	2	1

Empirical formula = CH$_2$O.

b Molecular ion at m/z = 60, so GFM of compound = 60 g.

GFM of CH$_2$O = 30 g, therefore molecular formula for compound is C$_2$H$_4$O$_2$.

Experimental determination of structure 2, pp. 74–75

Peak at 2962 cm^{-1} = C–H stretch.

Peak at 1750 cm^{-1} = C=O stretch in an ester.

$$H-\underset{\underset{H}{|}}{\overset{\overset{H}{|}}{C}}-\underset{\underset{H}{|}}{\overset{\overset{H}{|}}{C}}-O\overset{\diagdown}{}\underset{\underset{O}{\|}}{C}-\underset{\underset{H}{|}}{\overset{\overset{H}{|}}{C}}-H$$

Pharmaceutical chemistry, pp. 78–79

1

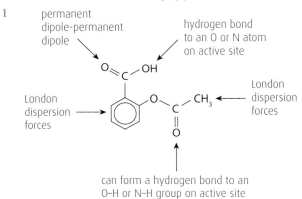

permanent dipole–permanent dipole

hydrogen bond to an O or N atom on active site

London dispersion forces

London dispersion forces

can form a hydrogen bond to an O–H or N–H group on active site

THINGS TO DO AND THINK ABOUT ANSWERS (CONT)

RESEARCHING CHEMISTRY

Gravimetric analysis, pp. 80–81

1   Number of moles of sodium carbonate in
    250 cm^3 = 0·1 mol l^{-1} × 0·25 l = 0·025 mol

    Mass of sodium carbonate = 0·025 × 106 g = 2·65 g

2   Number of moles of silver in silver(I) chloride $= \dfrac{107·9}{143·4}$
    $= 0·752$

Mass of silver in the precipitate	= 0·752 × 0·63
	= 0·474 g
Mass of silver in 1·00 litre solution	= 0·474 × 10
	= 4·74 g
% silver in the alloy	$= \dfrac{4·74}{10·48} \times 100$
	= 45 %

Volumetric analysis, pp. 82–83

You are given the volume and concentration of the sulfuric acid, so the number of moles of sulfuric acid can be calculated as
$n = V \times c = 0·0178 \times 0·220 = 0·003916$ mol.

The balanced stoichiometric equation for the reaction shows us that 2 mol of NaOH reacts with 1 mol of H_2SO_4:

$2NaOH + H_2SO_4 \rightarrow Na_2SO_4 + 2H_2O$

Therefore in the 25·0 cm^3 sample of the diluted drain cleaner there were 2 × 0·003916 = 0·007832 mol of NaOH.

In the 250 cm^3 standard flask, there must have been
0·007832 × 10 = 0·07832 mol of NaOH.

So in 10·0 cm^3 of the undiluted drain cleaner there was
0·07832 mol of NaOH

In one litre (1000cm^3) there would be
0·07832 × 1000/10 = 7·832 mol NaOH

The mass of NaOH = n × GFM = 7·832 × 40·0 = 313 g in 1 litre.

More on volumetric analysis, pp. 84–85

Number of moles of HCl added to the shell
= 0·500 × 0·025 = 0·0125 mol

Number of moles of NaOH used in titration
= 0·050 × 0·0225 = 0·001125 mol

$NaOH + HCl \rightarrow NaCl + H_2O$

So number of moles of HCl left unreacted = 0·01125 mol in 25 cm^3

Number of moles of HCl unreacted in 100 cm^3 = 0·0045 mol

Number of moles of HCl reacted with shells
= 0·0125 − 0·0045 = 0·008 mol

$CaCO_3 + 2HCl \rightarrow CaCl_2 + H_2O + CO_2$

So number of moles of calcium carbonate = 0·008/2 = 0·004 mol

Mass of calcium carbonate = 0·004 × 100 = 0·4 g

% $CaCO_3$ = 0·4/0·456 × 100 = 87·7%

Practical skills and techniques 2, pp. 88–89

1   0·00018 mol l^{-1}.

2   0·00018 mol l^{-1} in 100 cm^3 of standard solution.

$n = c \times V = 0\cdot00018 \times 0\cdot1 = 0\cdot000018$ mol

Mass of Mn $= n \times$ GFM $= 0\cdot000018 \times 54\cdot9 = 0\cdot0009882$ g

Therefore

% Mn in paper clip $= \dfrac{0\cdot0009882}{0\cdot24} \times 100 = 0\cdot41\%$.

Techniques used in the preparation and purification of compounds 1, pp. 90–91

1   The reaction was only heated for 10 minutes – reflux is used when mixtures need to be heated for a long time.

2   Add a small volume of hot ethanol to the aspirin and see if it dissolves. If any solid remains, add another small volume of hot ethanol. Place the aspirin–ethanol mixture on a hot-plate for one minute. If any solid remains, add another small volume of ethanol. Repeat until all the solid has dissolved. Carry out a hot filtration to remove any insoluble impurities and leave the filtrate to cool to room temperature. Filter the crystals.

3   Ethanol must be capable of dissolving aspirin when the solution is hot and aspirin must be less soluble in ethanol when cold. The impurities should be soluble in ethanol.

Techniques used in the preparation and purification of compounds 2, pp. 92–93

1   To remove more caffeine from the water layer as only a certain percentage of the caffeine is removed in each extraction.

2   The drying agent is used to remove any trace amounts of water remaining in the solvent mixture.

3   Ethyl ethanoate could be removed by distillation as it has a lower boiling point than caffeine.

Techniques used in analysing compounds, pp. 94–95

1   48%.

2   A sample of the synthesised aspirin could be spotted onto a TLC plate along with a spot of pure aspirin. A co-spot containing a little of both samples could also be spotted onto the plate. Once developed, a single spot for the co-spot would indicate that aspirin had been made. The R_f values could also be compared.

3   The melting point results suggest that the aspirin obtained is slightly impure. The temperature range is broad and the temperature is below the accepted melting point.

4   Recrystallisation.

INDEX